THE LANGUAGE OF LIFE

GEORGE W. BEADLE, Nobel Laureate in physiology and medicine and since 1961 President of the University of Chicago, has achieved distinction both in scientific research and in education. He received his B.S. and M.S. degrees from the University of Nebraska, his Ph.D. from Cornell, and has been a member of the faculties of Harvard, Stanford, and the California Institute of Technology. Dr. Beadle has served on various academic and governmental advisory committees and is a member of the National Academy of Sciences.

MURIEL BEADLE graduated from Pomona College in California and worked as an advertising copywriter in Chicago and Pasadena. Later, she was women's editor and feature writer for the Los Angeles *Mirror-News*. She is the author of *These Ruins Are Inhabited*.

The Language of Life

AN INTRODUCTION TO
THE SCIENCE OF GENETICS

BY

GEORGE AND MURIEL BEADLE

ANCHOR BOOKS
DOUBLEDAY & COMPANY, INC.
GARDEN CITY, NEW YORK

THE LANGUAGE OF LIFE was originally published by Doubleday & Company, Inc., in 1966. The Anchor Books edition is published by arrangement with Doubleday & Company, Inc.

Anchor Books edition: 1967

ILLUSTRATIONS BY JOSEPH M. SEDACCA, ROBERT G. BRYANT, AND JUAN C. BARBERIS

Excerpt from *African Genesis* by Robert Ardrey, copyright © 1961 by Literat S.A., is reprinted by permission of Atheneum Publishers and William Collins Sons & Company Ltd.

Sketches of Drosophila from *An Introduction to Genetics* by A. H. Sturtevant and G. W. Beadle, are reprinted by permission of Dover Publications, Inc.

Illustrations from "Tools and Human Evolution," *Scientific American*, September 1960; from "The Genetic Code," *Scientific American*, October 1962; and from "The Genetic Code: II," *Scientific American*, March 1963, are reprinted by permission of *Scientific American*.

Graph from *Report of the United Nations Scientific Committee on the Effects of Atomic Radiation*, General Assembly, 19th Session, Supplement No. 14 (A/5814), 1964, is reprinted by permission of the United Nations Publications Board.

*To Virginia and Vernon
and in Memory of Jess*

FOREWORD

In writing about genetics for non-scientists, the gap we have tried to bridge is not the one that is alleged to separate C. P. Snow's much-publicized two cultures, but the one that lies between people who received their formal schooling before the mid-fifties and those whose instruction in science has occurred since then.

An anecdote will illustrate the reason:

Not long ago, George was invited to speak to a society of physicians, all specialists in their particular branch of medicine, about the spectacular advances in biology that have recently taken place. Among those at the meeting was a college freshman named Bob, whose father had brought him along because of the boy's keen interest in science. After the meeting, several of the doctors ruefully confessed that they'd understood very little of the lecture; its terms and concepts were so unfamiliar that the whole thing seemed recondite. Bob, on the other hand, complained that the lecture had been so elementary that he hadn't learned anything new. "We had all that stuff in high school," he said.

These opposite reactions amused but did not surprise George. In recent years, the nation's schools (aided by a series of summer teachers' institutes supported by the National Science Foundation) have done a remarkable job of keeping abreast of developments in genetics. As a result, any lecturer on the subject now finds that his liveliest and most scientifically sophisticated audiences are composed either of teen-agers or of practicing research scientists.

On that account, this book is not written primarily for young people like Bob—although even they may find something of interest in it. The schools, perhaps unavoidably, tend to emphasize the acquisition of facts. The usual purpose of demonstrations and classroom experiments is to clarify and confirm something that is already known, not to discover something new. Consequently, the basic nature of scientific inquiry is sometimes confused with the body of information it produces or with the technology of its investigative methods—whereas, in truth, the heart of scientific inquiry and the source of the excitement it engenders in its practitioners lies not in the doing of experiments nor in the gathering of facts but in the application of imagination and intelligence to a problem. Likewise, the excitement of learning about science lies as much in following the reasoning behind the great discoveries as in knowing the results. Herein, therefore, we have viewed the history of genetics as a continuing (and far from completed) exercise in problem-solving. We hope that readers, of whatever age, will develop greater appreciation of science as the exhilarating intellectual adventure that we believe it is.

But that is an incidental goal. Our main objective has been to produce an easy-to-read and up-to-date book for anyone to whom DNA is a meaningless abbreviation—which is another way of describing great numbers of people whose study of biology culminated, ten or more years ago, with the dissection of a frog. To the same people, mention of the subspecialty of genetics too often brings to mind a picture of Gregor Mendel counting peas. It is important, of course, to know about Mendel (whose findings are still valid); but there is much more to know now, and that it be generally known is more important.

The new genetics is revolutionizing practices and investigative approaches in fields as diverse as medicine and the use of atomic power; therefore, every taxpayer or contributor to research institutions should understand the purposes for which his money is being sought or spent. In addition, the citizenry as a whole—not just the scientific fraternity within it—should thoroughly understand the genetic consequences of high-energy radiation, whether from X-rays or from fallout. To know how inherited diseases occur and are transmitted is desirable, too—both for the general reason that their increasing incidence affects the welfare of society, and for the specific help that such knowledge may provide people who have genetic diseases, as they approach marriage and parenthood.

The form and content of this book are based on public lectures that George, a geneticist since the 1930's, has given during recent years in an effort to summarize and simplify modern molecular biology for laymen. The writing was done by Muriel, who is not a scientist; in fact, until she attempted this book, she had learned only enough jargon to know that geneticists who refer to their children as F_1's are describing them quite precisely—if in scientific shorthand—as "first generation hybrids." The theory behind our collaboration, therefore, was that if George could explain genetics in terms simple enough for Muriel to grasp, *anybody* could understand it. It was our hope, initially, that we could do the job without using any language unfamiliar to non-scientists. This hope has not been realized. Scientific terminology has been held to a minimum, however; and Muriel insists that any moderately intelligent person can understand what we have written—unless he or she irrationally clings to an earlier-held conviction that science is *per se* incomprehensible.

For readers who wish to pursue this or related subjects, here are some suggestions for further reading:

The books in *Life* Magazine's Science Library—notably *The Cell* and *The Human Body*—are useful because of their many illustrations. *The Coil of Life,* by Ruth Moore (New York: Alfred A. Knopf, 1961) is on the same subject as this one, but its organization and emphasis make it quite different. Amram Scheinfeld's *Your Heredity and Environment* (Philadelphia: J. B. Lippincott Company, 1965)—an expanded and revised version of his famous *You and Heredity*—is an excellent layman's book on human genetics. It also includes an up-to-date list of heredity clinics, useful for people with genetic disease who desire professional counseling.

Only a little more demanding of the reader's concentrated attention than the books listed in the foregoing paragraph is Isaac Asimov's general science book, *The New Intelligent Man's Guide to Science* (New York: Basic

Books, 1965). Professor Asimov, a biochemist at Boston University, writes with clarity and grace.

Among the textbooks that non-scientists should at least look into—if only to read the complete story that we have sometimes oversimplified—are two books by professors at the University of California: Curt Stern's *Principles of Human Genetics* and Garrett Hardin's *Biology: Its Principles and Implications.* Both texts are published by W. H. Freeman & Company, San Francisco, the first in 1960, the second in 1961. *Heredity and Development,* by Columbia's John A. Moore (Oxford University Press, N.Y., 1963) and *Evolution, Genetics, and Man,* by Theodosius Dobzhansky (New York: John Wiley & Sons, 1963) are excellent paperbacks. Anything else written by Professor Dobzhansky, who is at the Rockefeller Institute, is worth reading, too. Also in paperback is a fine new book by J. D. Watson, *Molecular Biology of the Gene* (W. A. Benjamin, N.Y., 1965).

Finally, among periodicals, *Scientific American* belongs in the home of any literate person who wishes to be informed on new developments in science.

GEORGE *and* MURIEL BEADLE

Chicago
September 15, 1965

CONTENTS

THE LANGUAGE OF LIFE

Chapter 1

THE NEW SCIENCE OF HEREDITY

"Genetics" is a twentieth-century word and a twentieth-century science.

The word was coined by an English biologist, William Bateson, to designate that branch of biology which deals with the underlying causes of inherited resemblances and differences between individuals, and hence with the evolution of all living things.

Asserting that "the essential process by which the likeness of the parent is transmitted to the offspring . . . is as utterly mysterious to us as a flash of lightning to a savage," Bateson in 1902 exhorted his fellow biologists to engage more actively in the experimental study of heredity. He promised them that "an exact determination of the laws of heredity will probably work more change in man's outlook on the world, and in his power over nature, than any other advance in natural knowledge that can be clearly foreseen."

He was very nearly right. Man's ability to split the atom has probably worked more change in our outlook on the world and in our power over nature than any other twentieth-century advance in knowledge; but geneticists' discoveries about heredity and variation, and the effect of these upon evolution, are surely a close second. In the sixty-some years that have intervened since Bateson's quoted remarks appeared in the *Journal of the Royal Horticultural Society*,[1] the process by which the genes

1 This paper is included in *Mendel's Principles of Heredity, A Defence,* by W. Bateson (Cambridge University Press, 1902), a work undertaken as rebuttal to an anti-Mendel paper by Bateson's contemporary, W. F. R. Weldon. In addition to the historical value of its content, the book also preserves a classic example

(units of hereditary material) are transmitted from parent to child has become so well understood that man, alone among species, now possesses the ability to control his *own* evolution.

During the early decades of this century, genetics was regarded as one of the more exotic scientific disciplines. The eleventh edition of the Encyclopædia Britannica (1910–11) carried no entry on the subject, and the four-teenth edition (1939) disposed of it in three paragraphs. The study of heredity was then dominated by concern for the mechanics of inheritance. Were the genes physical entities? How did they make their passage from one gen-eration to the next? What caused them to change, and how were those changes expressed in the individual or-ganism? This line of inquiry is today called "classical ge-netics."

From the late thirties onward, the science of genetics took a biochemical turn. Its practitioners began to explore the workings of the genes—their structure, composition, and properties, and their dynamic role in the internal chemistry of living organisms. During the past decade there has been a burst of knowledge in this area. The current edition of the Encyclopædia Britannica (1965) includes fifteen pages on genetics, plus another two on the chemical nature of the gene.

---

of the paper wars that are still occasionally fought in the pages of scientific professional journals.

"It was with a regret approaching to indignation that I read Professor Weldon's criticism," Bateson begins. Later: "The reader who has the patience to examine Professor Weldon's array of ob-jections will find that almost all are dispelled by no more elaborate process than a reference to the original records." Finally, with a fine Victorian flourish: "Professor Weldon declares he has 'no wish to belittle the importance of Mendel's achievement'; he desires 'simply to call attention to a series of facts which seem to him to suggest fruitful lines of inquiry.' In this purpose I venture to assist him, for I am disposed to think that unaided he is—to borrow Horace Walpole's phrase—about as likely to light a fire with a wet dish-cloth as to kindle interest in Mendel's discoveries with his tempered appreciation. If I have helped a little in this cause my time has not been wasted."

Many distinguished investigators continue to explore classical (or "transmission") genetics, population genetics, or the effects of genes specifically upon man (human genetics, including applications to medicine). However, this book is written from the viewpoint of a biochemical geneticist—one who, upon rereading William Bateson's 1902 plea for increased experimental study of heredity, nods in agreement with Bateson's prediction that "the breeder, whether of plants or animals, will be second only to the chemist in resource and foresight. Each conception of life in which heredity bears a part—and which of them is exempt?—must change before the coming rush of facts."

Atoms are miniature solar systems, but at a level of smallness impossible to see and almost impossible to comprehend. They have three major components: protons and neutrons, which clump into a nucleus at the center of a space something like a trillionth of an inch in diameter; and electrons, which whirl around the nucleus billions of times each second.

All protons, neutrons, and electrons—whether they're in steel or in strawberry jam—are exactly alike. It's their number and position within an atom that distinguishes one element from another, and that gives different kinds of atoms their varying ability to combine into the groupings called molecules.

Hydrogen, the simplest element (and presumably the first), is made up of atoms in which only one electron circles the nucleus. But billions of years ago, in environments like the interior of our sun where temperature and pressure were and are incredibly high, hydrogen atoms fused to form helium atoms. Their nuclei are heavier than hydrogen's, and are circled by *two* electrons.

The same or similar processes (the sun is an efficient nuclear reactor) created atoms of increasing complexity. Lithium has three electrons, two in one ring and one in a farther-out ring. Beryllium has two and two. Boron, two and three. Carbon, two and four. Nitrogen, two and five. Oxygen, two and six. And so on, until eventually atoms with as many as 92 electrons whirling in seven different rings around nuclei of varying weights had been created.

Electrical charges are the atomic equivalent of nails or glue. They hold atoms—such as the hydrogen and oxygen of water or the sodium and chlorine of salt—together. It is difficult, when one lives in a world of seemingly solid substances, to think of them as nothing but infinitesimal particles held together in space by a force rather than by a thing. Perhaps it will help you to appreciate the essential quality of the atomic structure of matter if you compare it to a newspaper reproduction of a photograph, which under magnification is nothing but a series of dots, variously spaced to make light or dark areas. Instead of the dots, your eye sees the picture they form—just as you ordinarily see or feel the substances that atoms make up, instead of the atoms themselves.

Nine or ten billion years ago, the atoms of the various elements formed a monstrous cloud of cosmic dust. It is believed that part of the cloud became so dense that it coalesced into a sphere. Earth evolved from that sphere. The weight at the outside exerted pressure on the center, and finally a core of liquid iron was created. The surface began to form a crust of rock, and the space around it acquired the mantle of gases that men call air—only it wasn't the kind of air we breathe today. It had much less oxygen, and what oxygen it had was tied up with hydrogen in molecules of water.

Then there came a time when the water vapor in that air condensed on a grand scale to bring the oceans into being. The rains leached various compounds out of the rocky surface of the earth—phosphates, sulfates, fluorides; and in due course the seas became a vast but dilute soup of chemicals. These absorbed the invisible but high-energy ultraviolet rays of the sun. The result of such absorption was explosive: it caused the hydrogens and oxygens in water, the carbons and hydrogens in methane, the nitrogens and hydrogens in ammonia to recombine and form other kinds of molecules. These in turn gave rise to larger molecules such as those of alcohol and sugar. Eventually, some exceedingly large and complex molecules, many times the size of a molecule of hydrogen gas, came into

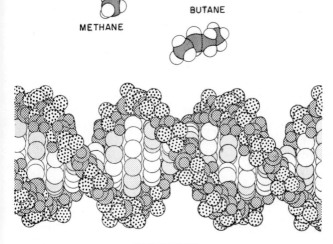

NUCLEIC ACID

Figure 1

being. Among them were the super-molecules that are called nucleic acids (*see Figure 1*). They were created perhaps three billion years after the earth was formed.

Nucleic acids were more than big . . . and complicated . . . and new. They had (and have) a unique property. Once made, they could (and can) initiate the making of copies of themselves. This ability, which they alone possess among molecules known to man, has made them the basis of all life on earth.

In the next chapter we will describe the structure of nucleic acids and the mechanics of their self-replication.

Chapter 2

THE MASTER MOLECULES OF LIFE

There are two kinds of nucleic acid. Both contain thousands of atoms of carbon, hydrogen, nitrogen, oxygen, and phosphorus—all arranged into subgroupings, molecules in their own right, before being combined into the large structure we showed in *Figure 1*. Among these subgroupings, in the kind of nucleic acid most important to our story, are six molecules (*see Figure 2A*) which we won't identify at the moment beyond telling you that they abounded in the primitive world, and that they are the building blocks of somewhat larger molecules called nucleotides. To make each nucleotide, the building blocks must be combined as shown in *Figure 2B*. Finally, a great many nucleotides—scores more than the four shown here—link to each other in the zigzag pattern shown in *Figure 2C*.

But that's only half the structure of nucleic acid. *Two* strands, composed as in the diagrams below, must come together as shown in *Figure 3*.

The resultant super-molecule doesn't have the flat, two-dimensional configuration of the diagram, however. Use your imagination, please, and envision the chemical building blocks at the bottom of the sketch as if they were closer to your eye, and those at the top as if they were farther from your eye than the building blocks in the center. Try to see the total as a corkscrew, or as a length of two-ply yarn. It may help to refer to *Figure 1;* there, the spiral structure of nucleic acid is obvious.

Two other points must also be made about this remarkable molecule.

First, the two chains "go" in different directions. They are, in fact, simply reversed—as if the nucleotides in one chain were swimmers floating with their faces up to the sun, and as if the nucleotides in the other chain were floating face down. To make this characteristic more

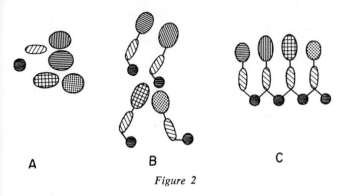

A   **B**   **C**

Figure 2

clear, we will now drop the shadings and patterns we have been using to distinguish one chemical building block from another; and we will substitute numbers for each of the four kinds of nucleotides—including reversed numbers for the nucleotides that are "floating face down" (*see Figure 4*).

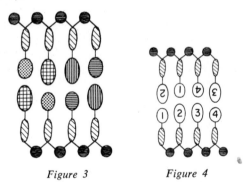

Figure 3   *Figure 4*

Secondly, notice that the nucleotides numbered 1 and 2 and those numbered 3 and 4 are paired—not 1 and 3 or 2 and 4. Among the hundreds and thousands of nucleotides that in reality make up a molecule of nucleic acid, any lengthwise sequence (not just the 1-2-3-4 sequence shown here) is possible, and any proportion of each kind of nucleotide. There may be twice as many 4's as 1's, for example. But there is one consistent rule (and to understand this is the secret of understanding why nucleic acid can make copies of itself): the 1's in one chain pair with the 2's in the other chain, and the 3's in one chain pair with the 4's in the other.

It's as if each were a wall plug with prongs spaced to fit a distinctive pattern of holes in a particular electric outlet. When nucleic acid makes a copy of itself, the "prongs" loosen (*Figure 5A*); the two chains drift apart, and the nucleotides in each now-separate chain are free to acquire new partners (*Figure 5B*). But note what happens if 1 tries to pair with 3, or 2 with 4 (*Figure 5C*). They don't fit. Hence, the proper reconstruction of each chain of nucleotides must wait until all nucleotides find their proper opposite numbers. And when that happens, *two* double chains have replaced the original *one* (*Figure 5D*).

Now, it is a convenient figure of speech to compare nucleotides to electric wall plugs and their outlets, in order to understand better their quality of complementarity. But nucleotides are not hard and unyielding like real wall plugs, and the structure we are talking about is submicroscopic. The "prongs" are hydrogen atoms, which form weak bonds between building blocks in paired nucleotides at those points where oxygen and nitrogen atoms or two oxygen atoms are properly opposed.

And once in a million times, just as a wall plug might come off the assembly line with correct interior circuitry but with misplaced prongs, a mistake in pairing can occur. *Figure 6* shows what would happen to a double chain of nucleic acid if 1 were to pair with 3—bearing in mind that a once-in-a-million mistake occurs, after all, only once in a million times; and that the process by which the nucleotides find partners is wholly mechanical. What would be made, after two replications, are three copies of the original molecule—and one different molecule, one in which the sequence of nucleotides has been altered. The process by which this change occurs is called mutation. Its result, in this example, is the creation of two kinds of nucleic acid molecules to replace the one kind that had existed in a prior generation. Such creation is of signal

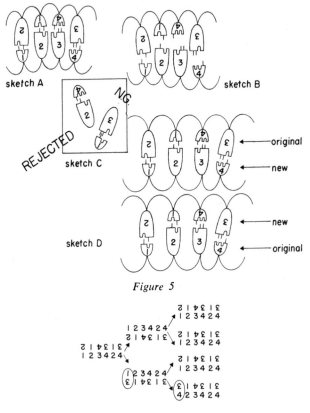

Figure 5

Figure 6

importance, because without it living things could not have evolved.

From the foregoing, you can see that the processes by which nucleic acids are formed and replicate and change are orderly—but not at all simple. Perhaps you can understand, therefore, why it took billions of years for nature to create them.

The phrase, "billions of years," has little meaning for most people. Few of us can really comprehend the magnitude of time; yet without such comprehension one has difficulty in appreciating the condition essential to the formation of nucleic acids. This comparison may help: suppose that all of the earth's history were to be compressed into an hour, thus making each 100,000,000 years one minute long; and that some cosmic observer had noted the position of the hands on the clock face at the time of which we now speak. The hands would have stood at thirty minutes past the hour. This is another way of saying that the earth is thought to be something like six billion years old, and that perhaps half of its history had elapsed before the nucleic acids came into being.

One is tempted to dramatize the appearance on earth of the only type of molecule known to man which can reproduce itself systematically, alter its character, and pass the alterations along to another generation of molecules. But at the time of the appearance of nucleic acids, there were no cheers . . . no blare of trumpets . . . no diarists to note that something important had happened on a certain day in a year that would come to be known as 2,980,001,965 B.C. (or whenever it happened). The beginnings of life were quiet and unheralded.

Some readers will dispute the assertion that molecules of nucleic acid, which we have described so unequivocally in chemical terms, were (or are) "alive." Yet one generally accepted definition of life is that the organism must be able to reproduce itself; to change; and to pass the changes along to its progeny. All of this the nucleic acids could (and can) do.

True, in the ancient time of their creation, their rate of replication must have been of a slowness beyond modern powers of comprehension, dependent as they were on finding just the right assortment of nucleotides clustered together in the nearby environment. It is probable, therefore, that for millions upon millions of years after their formation, the nucleic acids were the least in number among various kinds of molecules in the great chemical broth that was (and is) the sea. But once made, some of them endured; they evolved; and they became the master molecules of life.

Nucleic acid is the stuff your genes are made of. It

controls development and function. It is the biological bridge between the generations, transmitting a faithful copy of information carried in parental genes; or, as a result of mutation, creating progeny in some way uniquely different from their forebears. The survival of species depends upon the extent to which such differences affect the sons' and daughters' ability to maintain life in their particular environment, and to reproduce more of their kind. In short, nucleic acids are not only the chemical basis of life but also the raw material of evolution.

Chapter 3

CHEMICAL BUILDING BLOCKS OF LIFE

It has been said repeatedly that the spontaneous generation of life from non-living matter is an ancient superstition. And so it is, if one bases belief on the original evidence for belief—for example, that maggots arise spontaneously when meat decomposes. An Italian physician named Francesco Redi disposed of that idea in 1668; he covered meat with a layer of muslin and proved that maggots do not develop in meat unless flies can lay their eggs on it.

Microorganisms had been discovered at about the same time, but it took two more centuries to disprove that *they* were generated spontaneously by some vital force in the air. Louis Pasteur accomplished the job in 1862.

If not by spontaneous generation, then—how?

Maybe life has "always" existed? If so, not on earth, for geochemists have found by means of radioactive dating methods that the minerals in the rocks and soil of earth were formed five to ten billion years ago. Clearly, then, life on earth could not have originated before the planet *itself* was formed.

Perhaps it originated on another planet and came to earth as a passenger on a meteorite? The theory cannot be checked—at least not until the first spacecraft gets to Mars, or Venus, or beyond. But even if life did originate on another planet, the fundamental question of how it began would remain.

Perhaps by a supernatural event? As far as the earth is concerned, by Creation as described in the Bible? There was—and is—no way for science to prove or disprove this possibility, for by its very nature it is not subject to experimental investigation. However, one runs into all kinds of difficulties in trying to reconcile the Bible story with the fact that there was life on earth (as evidenced by fossils) for eons of time before the Flood. Furthermore, as the bones of various prehistoric men and submen began to turn up—in the Neanderthal valley in Germany, on the banks of a river in Java, in a South African stone quarry —investigators began to ask, "Which one was Adam?" And there was no answer.

But is special creation by *natural* forces ruled out? Many people are willing to accept the idea of evolutionary change in the direction of increasing complexity, but they want to start the journey with "true" life—not with a series of random chemical reactions in a primeval ocean. Couldn't some very simple one-celled organism have been generated complete? Alas, even the colon bacillus and the microscopic green alga, chlorella—which are among the simplest one-celled organisms known—are so complex in their structure that it stretches credibility to think of either as having been formed as the result of a single natural event.

So, in 1965, science has returned to the old belief that life originated spontaneously from non-living matter—but enough is now known about the nature of matter, living or otherwise, to make some highly informed guesses about the details of the process.

We said in the first chapter that hydrogen is the simplest of atoms, having only one electron whirling about its nucleus; and that other kinds of atoms have progressively more electrons and more rings around whose course the electrons orbit. That statement should now be amended: they aren't rings, in the sense of a circular track to which the electrons are confined. They are spherical areas in space, within which electrons move in various orbits and at varying distances from the nucleus; and they are called "shells."

If hydrogen, for example, were enclosed in a glass ball, its one electron would be seen moving in various patterns —but it would never get farther from the nucleus than the distance from the nucleus to the inner walls of the globe. Lithium would require two glass balls. And carbon would require three. Some atoms have as many as seven shells, in all of which the intra-atomic forces cause their electrons to behave as if something as rigid as glass were holding them within a certain space. (*See Figure 7.*)

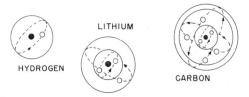

LITHIUM

HYDROGEN

CARBON

Figure 7

The capacity of the first shell is two electrons. Lithium and carbon are, as you see, at capacity. Outer shells can hold as many as eight electrons, but few atoms naturally have that many. What they have, instead, is a powerful propensity for getting them. If an atom has more than four electrons in its outer shells, it is likely to *take* the extras it needs from another atom. If it has less than four electrons in its outer shells, it is likely to *lose* them to another atom. Sometimes it *shares* electrons. It is this propensity for giving, taking, or sharing that holds atoms together and causes them to form molecules.

Let us examine more closely the element carbon. It's a very special case, because it has exactly four electrons in its outer shells. It can either lose them, gain four more, or share them—a property that enables it to combine with other atoms in more ways than any other kind of atom is capable of doing. Carbon can hitch other atoms into long straight chains, branched chains, rings, double rings, and many other structural patterns: more than any Tinker Toy set you played with as a child; and, like those juvenile masterworks, each has a unique identity. (*See Figure 8.*) In short, carbon can build exceedingly complicated molecules. Because of that capability, it is the basis of life on earth.

If you learned your chemistry twenty or thirty years ago, you learned that there were two kinds of substances: organic and inorganic, which originally were equated with

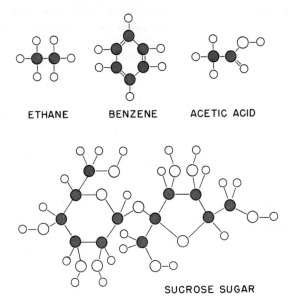

ETHANE   BENZENE   ACETIC ACID

SUCROSE SUGAR

* CARBON ATOMS IN SHADED AREAS

Figure 8

"from living organisms" or "from inert matter." The new definition of organic is "complex carbon-containing molecules." Everything else is inorganic.

It has been estimated that the seas of three billion years ago were dilute solutions in which more than 99 per cent of the dissolved substances were inorganic. Salt is an example. But among the other less than 1 per cent were several kinds of complex carbon-containing molecules:

1. Sugars of several kinds. Glucose, the kind found in grapes, is among the simplest in atomic structure.

2. Amino acids. These substances are distinguished by the way in which they combine a group of atoms containing nitrogen (an "amino group") with a second group of atoms whose character is acidic. There are twenty or more kinds of amino acids, and if you chain them together in certain numbers and combinations, they become

proteins. Proteins are among the most important components of any living organism. Blood contains proteins. So does muscle. And hair. And feathers.

3. Substances of which it is characteristic that carbon and nitrogen atoms are linked together in ring formations: a single ring in *thymine* and *cytosine;* a double ring in *adenine* and *guanine.* Any one of the four can combine with a sugar and with a phosphate group (phosphorus plus four oxygen atoms) to form a big molecule called a nucleotide. It is shown in *Figure 9,* together with the simpler diagram of the same structure that we used in a previous chapter.

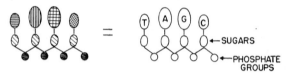

Figure 9

Nucleotides incorporating thymine and those incorporating adenine have a peculiar affinity for each other. Whenever this particular twosome is formed so that certain of their oxygen or nitrogen atoms are in the right position relative to each other, the two compounds will fit together like clasped hands. The same is true for cytosine- and guanine-containing nucleotides.

The "right" position requires that individual members of a pair be oriented in opposite directions; then, hydrogen bonds between specific atoms will hold the two nucleotides together (*see Figure 10*). You have already seen this kind of joining; and have undoubtedly guessed that the nucleotides numbered 1 and 2 in the second chapter were those you now know as containing thymine and adenine. Those numbered 3 and 4 contain guanine and cytosine. From now on we will use the first initials of their names, instead of numbers.

The building blocks of such molecules almost certainly existed in the ancient oceans. If they came together in the right circumstances they would have combined into

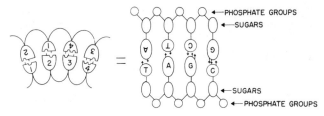

Figure 10

nucleotides and then into chains of nucleotides. It may be that, in some quiet primeval pool or puddle, the first significant (significant to man, that is) pairing of nucleotides occurred as in *Figure 11A.* Or perhaps single chains formed first; two chains composed of exactly complementary molecules happened to drift past each other; and they joined, as shown in *Figure 11B.* In either case, a primitive nucleic acid molecule would have been created.

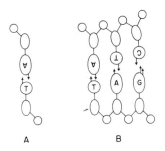

A   B

Figure 11

There is no reason why such chains of nucleotides couldn't have grown longer as a result of the same circumstances that brought them together in the first place. There is no reason why they couldn't have become varied to include any sequence of A, T, G, or C, or any proportion of each. And there is no reason why any couplet or chain couldn't have split apart and replicated itself—given enough time to find the right partners, A for T and C for G. There *was* enough time; at least three billion years. There was enough ocean; two-thirds of the

globe was covered by it. And there was a sufficient supply
of raw materials, the sun's rays having provided abundant
energy for their synthesis.

Nobody knows if it really happened that way. No one
was around to take notes. But there is impressive evidence
in support of the possibility:

In 1938, the Russian biochemist A. I. Oparin suggested
that organic compounds of the sort we have just mentioned—the sugars, the amino acid building blocks of
protein, and the nucleotides—could have arisen only in a
world with little free oxygen (for reasons we'll discuss in
the next chapter). Astronomers and geophysicists have
good reason to believe that the early atmosphere of the
earth was deficient in oxygen, and have been able to trace
the initial distribution of the elements on this and other
planets.

As a result of such research, the American physicist
Harold Urey postulated in 1952 that the primeval atmosphere of the earth consisted largely of methane, ammonia, hydrogen, and water. Subsequently, a graduate
student in his University of Chicago laboratory, Stanley
Miller, tested the possibility of organic compounds arising
in such an environment. Upon discharging a high-fre-
quency electric spark into a "primeval atmosphere" (which
necessarily was under glass in the laboratory), he found
two amino acids and formaldehyde, which is a precursor
of glucose sugar.

Later, he and other investigators, also simulating conditions of the primitive earth and supplying energy equivalent to the sun's ultraviolet rays or a lightning flash, witnessed the spontaneous generation of still more amino
acids—sometimes single ones, sometimes several chained
together into molecules like small proteins. Still other
experiments have produced adenine, guanine, a substance
closely related to thymine but which is called uracil, and
a couple of kinds of sugar.

Let's go back to one point. Either in the laboratory or
in the ancient world, were these organic molecules created
by chance, in the sense of casually and without predestina-

tion? Or was their formation a certainty, in the sense of intended and fully predictable?

The difference between a chance event and a predictable one is merely a difference in degree of probability. If the probability is .001—that is, one in a thousand—of an event happening within twenty-four hours, we are inclined to call it a chance event; whereas a probability of .999—or 999 chances in a thousand, for the same period of time—causes us to regard the event as almost a certainty. Suppose, then, that one increases the time-span for the event with .001 probability to billions of years. The probability of its occurring closely approaches certainty.

Remember that chemists cannot initiate reactions that could not take place in nature. They can only arrange favorable circumstances and thus increase the probability that a reaction will take place. It follows, therefore, that if the right sequence of circumstances came about on early earth, it was as inevitable that the atoms in methane, hydrogen, ammonia, and water would rearrange themselves into amino acids or the components of nucleic acid as when it happens in modern laboratories.

In sum: although no one knows that it did happen that way, it could have—and no better explanation has been put forward.

Chapter 4

THE EVOLUTION OF LIFE

In the second chapter, we said that a mistake in pairing of nucleotides can—on very rare occasions—occur, and we compared the physical structure of a molecule that permits such pairing to a wall plug which had come off the assembly line with correct interior circuitry but with misplaced prongs.

The chemical explanation of such a structure is that certain atoms in one molecule have shifted position slightly, enough to permit hydrogen bonds to form between the two molecules at the wrong points. The odds against such a union are enormous, but as in unions between human partners who are obviously mismatched, once in a while they beat the odds.

In *Figure 12* we repeat a diagram you've seen before—substituting for the numbers we first used the initials standing for thymine and adenine, guanine and cytosine.

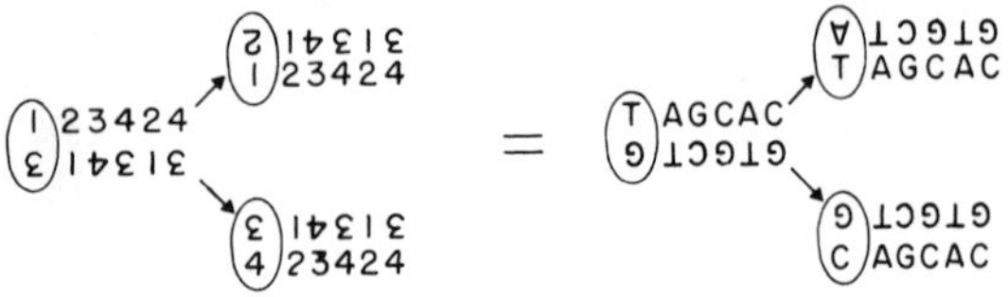

Figure 12

They *should* pair as written in the foregoing sentence, but when—on very rare occasions—thymine pairs with guanine you get a maverick molecule like the one shown here. However, when the two strands of that molecule separate and the nucleotides in each seek new partners for themselves, they are more likely to pick their natural complements—special circumstances by their very nature being unlikely to recur. The top chain would reconstitute itself so that thymine would pick up adenine, and the bottom chain would pair guanine with cytosine. Thus, two nucleic acid molecules of different character—different by only one nucleotide pairing, but nevertheless different—would have come into being. Another way of saying the same thing is to say that a mutation had occurred.

Given enough time, mutations of this sort could have caused the creation of an almost infinite variety of nucleotide sequences among nucleic acids. And with the appearance of this variety, the conditions of life (or at least the conditions of life according to one definition) would have been met: that an organism be able to reproduce itself, to change, and to pass the change on to another generation.

Thus, we have come again to the point in time when the cosmic clock stood at half past the hour—or three billion years ago.

The years continued to tick away, each 100,000,000 years being one minute long. As in the beginning, simple molecules continued to be formed. They continued to be the building blocks of larger molecules like the nucleic acids and the proteins. And, eventually, two of these large molecules combined: a nucleic acid molecule with a protein molecule. The protein became a protective coat for the nucleic acid—a great advantage, because the nucleic acid now had partial armor against the forces that tear molecules apart.

This new nucleoprotein molecule was also a little more complex than its predecessor, the nucleic acid molecule, for it had to develop the ability to make a protein coat for itself whenever it duplicated. That such was the case is suggested by the presence on earth today of organisms which are nothing but nucleic acid encased in protein—and since only nucleic acid can make copies of itself, it *must* incorporate somewhere in its "memory" the directions for making the protein of its coat. Perhaps nucleotides are like letters of the alphabet, inert until they are put together in certain sequences? Then they acquire meaning and can give directions—as when "g" and "o" unite to say "go."

Let's call that nucleoprotein molecule a "protogene." In at least one respect, the world it inhabited was somewhat different from the world of, say, 500,000,000 years before its formation. There weren't quite so many organic compounds available as building blocks for living organisms. And here's why:

From the beginning of earth, water molecules (two atoms of hydrogen and one of oxygen—H_2O) had been splitting apart in the upper reaches of the atmosphere. Because its atoms are very small and light, much of the freed hydrogen had gone whipping off into space, leaving much of the oxygen behind. Many of these oxygen atoms had combined by threes into molecules of ozone (O_3). And little by little a thin band of ozone had begun to veil the earth, miles above its surface.

Ozone absorbs ultraviolet radiation as if it were a blotter; and so, as the upper-atmosphere band of ozone increased in density, the amount of ultraviolet light that reached the earth was gradually reduced. The long rays of sunlight—the visible part—still got through; but it was UV light that knocked molecules apart, put their atoms together in new combinations, and provided the energy for the making of organic compounds from methane, ammonia, hydrogen, and water.

Given these circumstances, suppose that a protogene mutated in such a way that it became capable of making for itself an organic substance needed for its growth and function, a substance which it had been obtaining ready-made in the sea but which had now—with the reduction in UV light—become difficult to find.

To be more specific, suppose that, in order to form its protein coat, a protogene needed a certain amino acid—arginine, say, and that arginine was scarce. Any protogene that mutated so that it could convert some other substance, one that was still plentiful, into arginine would have achieved more independence from its environment than sister organisms which had *not* mutated in the direction of greater self-sufficiency.

But to break down one substance and change it into another is a fairly complicated chemical reaction. Nature has provided living systems with some specialist molecules whose job is just that. They are called enzymes. Organic chemical reactions can take place without them, but only at a very slow pace. They bring things to a speedier conclusion than would otherwise be possible, and in a complex organism are absolutely necessary to control the timing of a multitude of delicately interlocked chemical reactions.

Enzymes are proteins. If nucleic acid could make the protein of its protective coat, there is no reason why the directions for doing so couldn't be amended—by changing or adding a sequence of nucleotides—to specify the making of *another* kind of protein. In fact, the coat itself could contain proteins with different roles in the life of the organism.

Furthermore, enzymes are highly specific; that is, each controls just one small chemical reaction. This fact is consistent with the hypothesis that 1) a protogene could have mutated in such a way that it could make an enzyme and that 2) such a mutant would be preferentially multiplied—"selected"—whenever it served a useful purpose.

Let us digress for a moment to discuss one often-misunderstood fact about mutation, using a modern example.

It is obvious that spraying flies with DDT has not rid the world of flies. The reason is that in every sprayed population of flies, a few were in some way slightly different from the others, the difference having been caused by a prior mutation in the nucleic acid of their parents' genes. This difference was passed on to them, and made them resistant to DDT. Therefore they survived the spraying, and produced more of their kind.

Note that the presence of DDT did not "cause" the beneficial (from the flies' point of view) mutation; instead, its presence suddenly conferred an advantage upon its possessors. Likewise, scarcity of arginine in the primitive sea did not "cause" protogenes to mutate so they could make enzymes that would convert some more

plentiful substance to arginine. The appropriate mutations had already occurred at random in the protogene
population, and suddenly became useful.

Suppose now that the substance from which a primitive
organism made arginine in *its* turn grew scarce? If that
organism, the one that produced an enzyme capable of
changing the second substance into arginine, were to
unite with an organism possessing enzymes capable of
making the second substance from yet a third substance
—C→B→A—the double organism would have a survival
advantage over *its* kinfolk. It would, in addition, have become an organism with two genes—*true* genes, because of
their ability to make enzymes.

And if a ribbon of nucleic acid could incorporate the
ability to direct the making of one and then two enzymes,
why couldn't it later develop the capacity to make three,
four, or more? So, stepwise backwards: G→F→E→D→
C→B→A. The nucleic acid would, of course, have to re-
tain the ability to make its full complement of enzymes
each time it replicated, and therefore it would have added
more nucleotides with each mutation that brought a new
enzyme into being.

Thus, just as libraries grow larger as the need to store
information increases, so living things over the millennia
must have tended to increase in size and complexity with
each new mutation—evolving from raw nucleic acid to
nucleoprotein "protogenes" to one-gene, one-enzyme systems to multi-gene, multi-enzyme systems of the sort that
are all around us today, the kind that *we* are.

This step-by-step theory of their development was proposed in 1945 by the American biochemist Norman Horo-
witz. We do not know if it happened as described, but
we do know of many organisms today that under experimental observation undergo mutation in a way that
causes proteins to acquire enzymatic activity that they
did not have before. There is, for example, a bacterium
which is sensitive to the antibiotic penicillin. If millions
of such bacterial cells are placed in a culture containing
penicillin, the great majority of them fail to multiply.
But a few—perhaps one in a million—survive. They do

so because a sequence of nucleotides that carries directions for making a certain protein has in their case alone been altered—and in their case alone an enzyme is produced that inactivates the penicillin.

Such cases are not unique. Many other gene mutations are known which result in the production of enzymatically active proteins which have inactive counterparts in other individuals of the same species. Therefore it is easy to imagine that, over a long stretch of time, a given kind of organism could have developed the ability to make many useful enzymes as a result of a series of small changes which were cumulative in effect.

Chapter 5

LIFE GROWS GREEN

Perhaps you have been thinking, "It's all very well to talk about an organism's ability to synthesize substances needed for growth and function—but that's only a result. What powers the action? What's the process?"

The process is called metabolism. (The word comes from the Greek *metabolos,* meaning "changeable.") Metabolism is the total of all the closely coordinated, delicately balanced chemical reactions used by an organism to cause certain raw materials to release energy. This energy is then used in a controlled way to combine other raw materials into substances needed for growth and function.

Now, where do raw materials get the energy they release?

Energy comes in many forms, all of which are readily convertible to other forms. When you rub cold hands together, for one example, the energy of motion turns into the energy of heat. Electrical energy becomes light energy when you flip a switch. Light energy converts into electrical energy when a photoelectric cell opens a supermarket door for you. When coal burns, chemical energy changes to heat. And so on and on and on. Energy is never lost; it is simply changed from one form to another; and with every transformation it does some work.

The source of energy fundamental to life is sunlight. Its ultraviolet rays, as we said earlier, were the force that first tore molecules apart and recombined their atoms into new molecules, some of which were organic and some of which were not. Among the inorganic molecules there is one with a "tail" composed of three phosphate groups (phosphorus joined to oxygen). They are aligned in a 1-2-3 string. The radiant energy that strung them together is locked into them—until something causes the one farthest out to split off from the others. When that happens, chemical energy is released. It is this chemical energy that powers the metabolic machinery of all living organisms.

The ocean was full of these high-energy phosphates for a long time. From a supply always replenished by the action of UV light, evolving organisms took what they needed. As the more complicated organisms developed, they created enzymes whose job was to split off that final phosphate group. The energy so released was used by different kinds of organisms to run their metabolic machinery in different ways—but all were (and are) dependent on using it.

Then came the pinch. During the many millions of years that it took the multi-gene, multi-enzyme systems to evolve—from the time that the hands of the cosmic clock stood at perhaps thirty-five minutes past the hour until they reached four minutes of the next hour—the blanket of ozone in the upper atmosphere had been getting denser. Primitive organisms had themselves contributed to it, because the by-product of their metabolism was carbon dioxide (one atom of carbon, two of oxygen— CO_2). Eventually some of that oxygen found its way upward and helped further to diminish the amount of ultraviolet light that reached the earth's surface. Fewer organic molecules, of all kinds, were made spontaneously. And in time even the new do-it-yourself organisms were affected. The ingenious ways they had found for converting abundant substances into scarce substances were useless if they lacked the energy necessary to power those conversions, and supplies of high-energy phosphates were shrinking too.

Then—at four minutes of the hour, which is the same thing as saying 400,000,000 years ago—an event of stupendous importance to us as human beings took place. Some one of the multi-gene, multi-enzyme organisms incorporated into its structure a very complex molecule called chlorophyll, a molecule that must already have had its own long evolutionary history. Chlorophyll is the stuff that makes plants green. More importantly, it is a spectacularly good energy-converter. Its atomic structure is such that its electrons change the energy in ordinary sunlight—the visible rays—into chemical energy in the form of high-energy phosphates. Thus, when incorporated into a living organism, it frees that organism from dependence on ultraviolet light.

Chlorophyll created the physical environment to which nature's response was the evolution of all oxygen-using organisms.

The process to which chlorophyll is the key is called photosynthesis. Photosynthesis uses carbon dioxide and water as its raw materials. Both were, and are, abundant in nature. Starting with six molecules each of carbon dioxide and water, the energy of sunlight plus chlorophyll plus enzymes plus phosphates (and other things) finally results in the formation of a molecule of glucose sugar and high-energy phosphate. Such molecules become the organism's "energy bank." Some of the original oxygen is not needed for this reaction and is released into the air.

The most important evolutionary consequence of photosynthesis was that it introduced, for the first time, substantial amounts of free oxygen into the terrestrial environment —not oxygen tied up in various kinds of molecules, to be freed by later breakdown, but pure oxygen. As a result:

1. Even more oxygen was available to rise into the upper atmosphere and increase the amount of UV-absorbing ozone, thus further reducing the amount of UV light that reached earth. Eventually, this created famine conditions for those primitive organisms which were still dependent on finding organic materials ready-made in the sea, and many of them became extinct.

2. Any of the more self-sufficient organisms which incorporated chlorophyll now acquired a great advantage over similar organisms which did not. Photosynthesis, although it starts with a weaker energy source than UV light, is a highly efficient "booster" operation; and organisms that use it end up with fifteen times as much chemical energy on tap as organisms which do not use it. Therefore, the first chlorophyll-containing organisms—pre-

cursors, no doubt, of the aquatic plants called algae—must have multiplied explosively.

3. Since ordinary sunlight is so abundant and photosynthesis delivers so much energy, any chlorophyll-containing organism can make more raw materials than it needs at the moment. Such ability creates a use for storage space within the organism.

Rudimentary storage space was probably already at hand: millions of years before, the agglomeration of raw materials drawn from the sea—awaiting processing, as it were—must have formed a loose congregation of molecules surrounding the protogenes; and from that mass a containing membrane could have evolved. Now, if space within that membrane could be used also for the storage of excess raw materials, the organism would have the equivalent of a pantry shelf of canned goods—for it, as for a modern housewife, a reserve against future need. And chlorophyll-containing organisms had the capacity to make just such an excess.

Thus, probably, cells arose. A cell consists of a nucleus, which is the site of its nucleic acid; and of a surrounding mass of cytoplasm (*see Figure 13*). Cytoplasm is important to the living cell for many reasons, but one of its important jobs is to store materials needed for growth. A human egg cell, for example, is rich in cytoplasm while a sperm cell is not. Because the offspring will develop within the egg cell, that's where nature puts the food.

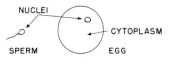

Figure 13

4. The diminishing amount of ultraviolet light meant that living organisms were less likely to be destroyed by its high-energy rays, and more of them survived to reproduce. They came up from the shielding depths of the ocean and floated more freely on its surface. Eventually,

one of the algae got established ashore, an event that marked the beginning of the land plants' evolution.

5. With so much free oxygen now available, any organism that could use oxygen in its metabolic processes had a happy future. The last step, therefore, was the development of living things which did not have to engage in photosynthesis themselves but could use oxygen to utilize the energy locked in the cells of plants. Thus animals came into being. The great self-perpetuating cycle of life was, with them, complete, for their metabolic system is the reverse of the green plants': they take in oxygen and excrete carbon dioxide, and thus restore to the plants an essential raw material.

It had taken almost three billion years for life to progress from raw molecules of nucleic acid to the highly elaborate structure characteristic of even the humblest flatworm. What has happened since has been incredibly fast—on the cosmic time scale. The hands of the heavenly clock stood somewhere within the last minute of the hour when knee-high ancestors of the modern horse first grazed their way across some African veld. And it was less than a second ago that a group of ape men—in physiology and behavior already foreshadowing the true men who would be their descendants—first ran erect across that same veld with spears in hand, in joint pursuit of the bigger horse that had evolved from the earlier ones.

What's the evidence for the speculations about the evolution of life as drawn in this and foregoing chapters? It's all indirect, but . . .

The nucleic acids are the same in all living things; it is merely the differing sequence of nucleotides that spells out the differences among species and individuals. All living systems require high-energy phosphates in their metabolism. The proteins in all living things (and in fossils, too) are made of the same amino acids—not only the same in chemical composition but also in configuration.

This latter point requires explanation. Amino acids, as formed in laboratory re-creations of primeval earth conditions, may have one of two configurations, the difference being comparable to the difference between your right and left hands. Neither configuration is "better" in the sense that an amino acid is more or less an amino acid —yet the amino acids that one finds in living organisms today are virtually without exception L-amino acids, those with the left-handed configuration.

In sum, then, the deeper that investigators probe into the cells of living creatures, the clearer it becomes that all forms of life must have had a common ancestor. That ancestor was a nucleic acid molecule which incorporated protein and, fueled by high-energy phosphates, learned how to make more protein when it replicated. It developed specialized enzymes to help it mesh the increasingly complicated chemical reactions necessary to self-synthesis of its building blocks. It learned to duplicate these enzymes, too, whenever it reproduced itself. A particular organism with this background was the first to make successful use of chlorophyll. It happened to make its proteins from L-amino acids. It is from that particular organism—the first green alga in the sea, perhaps—that we descend.

And here's a concluding fact to think about the next time you're waiting beside your radio or TV to hear whether an astronaut has made it home. It is conceivable that some combination of organic materials other than the one characteristic of the nucleic acids might be called "alive," and perhaps such life exists on another planet. On the earth, however, no fundamentally different organization of the raw materials of life is now possible. Those raw materials are still being spontaneously created by the action of ultraviolet light, but they can no longer drift in peace in the waters of a sterile ocean until the slow processes of time and chance combine them into more complex structures. Living organisms already in existence devour newly formed organic compounds as soon as they are created; they have no opportunity to evolve into anything.

It is true that during the three billion years or so since life began, its course has followed a multiplicity of channels—witness the infinite variety of living things—and presumably will continue to do so. But insofar as the basic chemistry of life is concerned, nature cannot now go back to the beginning and try again.

Chapter 6

THE EVOLUTION OF MAN

There was no timetable and no hurry. There was no blueprint for the evolution of any species, no developmental goal for any organism—other than its own imperative of maintaining and reproducing itself.

Three hundred million years ago, as now, the vast majority of plants and animals made exact duplicates of themselves. Their descendants—the one-celled algae and the one-celled protozoa—are still around. But in every generation of every kind of organism, some genes were, and are, altered by chance, thus making the organism somewhat different from its predecessors.

Most such alterations were, and are, harmful: even the simplest protozoan has such delicately balanced internal machinery that a random change is more likely to throw a wrench into the works than to improve their operation. (Think of your watch: what are the odds that dropping it will improve its accuracy as a timepiece?) Therefore, most mutations result either in the outright death of the individual organism, or in a weakening that reduces the ability of the species to reproduce—which causes death on the installment plan.

But once in a while, a mutation confers a slight advantage over other organisms competing for the same food or space. It is that mutation which makes evolution possible.

Robert Ardrey[1] describes the difference between the useless and useful mutation by a lively analogy with poker:

You hold the ten, jack, queen, and king of hearts, along with the nine of spades. The nine gives the other cards a considerable value, and you are in business with a high straight. But discard the nine of spades and draw. If you draw a lesser

[1] In *African Genesis* (New York: Atheneum, 1961).

card, then you are out of the game. Your ten, jack, queen, and king of hearts are suddenly of no value; you have suffered a normal mutation, and you are dead. Or you may draw a higher card, any but an ace. Your high straight is gone, and you are reduced to a pair. You are not dead, but suffer many such hands and you will be out of the game. Draw the ace of hearts, however, and every other card will leap in value. You will have a royal flush, the pot on the table, and in all probability a heart attack. In only this last qualification does such a draw differ from a benevolent mutation.

In the ancient world, where life dwelt more comfortably in water than on land, one-celled organisms must have drifted together by accident, each cell remaining a complete individual (as is still true of the sponges); and then a colony of cells must have merged into a supraorganism in which cells took on specialized functions. In time, nucleic acid carried directions for a multitude of different kinds of cells: some became muscle, others developed sensory capacities and became part of the nervous system, still others began their evolution into blood cells and bones.

The most primitive of such multicellular animals were only two cell layers thick. (Some descendants of such creatures, like the jellyfish, have never progressed beyond this stage.) Then a third cell layer evolved, and with it the two great groups of the animal kingdom took their initial fork in the evolutionary road. It is from that third cell layer that all organs of the animal grow. In one large group it gives rise to creatures with backbones, and animals in that group are called vertebrates. Man is a vertebrate. Of the other group—the invertebrates—the insects are the most highly developed modern example.

Primitive animals, already differentiated in one fundamental way (presence or absence of a backbone), grew progressively more differentiated as the ages passed. Whenever a given series of modifications finally created a distinctively new type of animal, a series of subtypes invariably developed—each adapted to different habits of life within the environment that had shaped the physiology

of the group as a whole. And those subtypes further differentiated themselves from each other.

It has been fashionable in the past to describe the
evolution of living organisms in terms of a ladder or
chain. That's why the "missing link"—the creature alleged to lie between man and apes—was long sought.
But such comparisons give a false picture. The forms of
life do not necessarily lead into a next logical form.
(What would the next step following the dinosaurs have
been, if there had been one?) Some peter out early,
experimental models that didn't quite make a place for
themselves. Some vanish abruptly, perhaps victims of
overspecialization. (Like manufacturers of buggy whips, in
the early 1900's.)

Visualize a tree and follow its branching from trunk
into a series of major limbs, from each of which sprout
other limbs, and from each of these, still more; until
the tree at its periphery is a close-meshed network of
small branches with twigs at their tips. Each twig is
linked to the parent trunk by the multiple branchings
that created it—and in that sense each twig is kin to all.
Yet each twig is unique in the space it occupies, and different in appearance from parts of the tree that were formed
earlier. This is far enough to take the analogy of trees and
evolution, for all the twigs on a real tree are alike, whereas

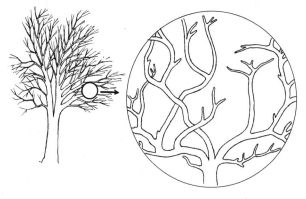

Figure 14

on the tree of life, the "twigs" arising from each major branching, and the branches, too, differ as much in appearance and function as reptiles differ from fish or as birds and mammals differ from reptiles.

Just so, by successive branchings from common stock, animal life in its wide diversity evolved over a period of millions of years. The development of sexual reproduction was a step of great moment in the diversification of species, for it created individuals whose characteristics arose from the pooled genes of two parents rather than being copied from just one.

Remember, however, that no single individual differed markedly from its parent—only from its ancestors or its descendants many hundreds of generations removed.[2] That now-extinct fish which first managed to swap gills for lungs did not itself sire the land-living lizards, nor was there an abrupt transition from cold-blooded reptiles to warm-blooded birds or mammals; in fact, it is estimated that it took 14,000,000 years for the most primitive mammals to develop from reptiles. ("Cold-" or "warm-" bloodedness is actually not descriptive of blood temperature, but of an animal's ability to maintain an even internal temperature despite temperature changes in its environment. Warm-blooded creatures do this better, thus have greater mastery over their environment.) The forms of life overlap, and the story of evolution is one of intermediates.

---

[2] As late as the 1940's, the point was still being argued. The American zoologist Richard Goldschmidt built quite a case for his belief that multiple concurrent changes could have created new species. A reptile, for example, could have changed into a bird—if enough changes in its structure had occurred within one generation. Goldschmidt developed an ingenious argument in support of how this might have happened.

However, since there are thousands of differences between reptiles and birds, most scientists were not persuaded—especially when someone realized that the several thousand changes would have had to occur to *two* reptiles at the same time and in the same place, since one needs both a male and a female to perpetuate a species. Goldschmidt's hypothesis has come to be known as "the hopeful monster" theory.

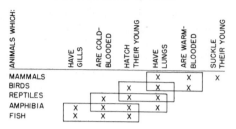

Figure 15

Look at the overlaps in vertebrate evolution as shown in *Figure 15*.

During his lifetime, man cannot observe evolution in himself or in the higher animals because the pace is too slow. But we have found fossil remains of reptiles with wings and feathers, and there are animals extant—living fossils, really—which exemplify progressively more developed stages of mammalian life. Still on the threshold, for example, is the platypus, a creature whose pedigree must go back 160,000,000 years to the time of the dinosaurs. An egg-layer like birds and reptiles, the platypus suckles her young once they are hatched. A next developmental stage is represented by marsupials like the kangaroo, who give birth to young so immature that they perish unless they are returned immediately to the shelter of the mother's body. The final advance in mammalian physiology was the evolution of the placenta, which enables the young to develop fully in the womb. Placental mammals —moles, foxes, whales, camels, apes, men—are in the vast majority of mammals today.

Apes and men are more alike than moles are like foxes or foxes are like whales; which is another way of saying apes and men are adjacent twigs far out on one branch of the tree of life. Much farther back in time—closer to the branchings that led to moles or foxes or whales—there was a precursor of both apes and men. That precursor was probably a tree-shrew the size of a modern squirrel, distinctive from other animals of its period (perhaps 70,-000,000 years ago) because it had those characteristics which have caused its descendants to be called primates. Instead of paws, for example, it had toes and fingers, with the thumb and big toe already divergent. It had big eyes and eye sockets. Certain body mechanisms gave it unusual ability to maintain balance in a shifting and swaying arboreal environment. And the parts of the brain that control vision and motor coordination were correspondingly well developed (by comparison with other mammals of the time).

The brain has an ancient history; it appears in the very simplest vertebrates. It evolved as a complement to special sensory cells which enabled primitive animals to react to objects at a distance—an ability which gave them a selective advantage, of course, for they could then avoid danger and live to reproduce. In time, the brain developed various sections, the evolutionary trend over the ages having been for the sections that control behavior to have developed successively farther from the spinal cord in successively higher animals. ("Higher," incidentally, means organisms whose increasing complexity of parts is paralleled by the increasing ability of all parts to function together as a unified whole.)

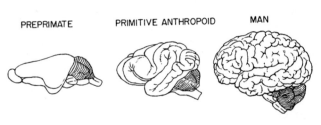

PREPRIMATE   PRIMITIVE ANTHROPOID   MAN

Figure 16

That frontal part of the brain called the cerebral cortex began in fish and amphibians as little more than a thickening of tissue. By the time birds evolved, it had become the site of vision. Its growth in mammals was much greater, both quantitatively and qualitatively. Finally, in such advanced primates as apes and men, the cerebral cortex grew so large in area that it had to fold in on itself in order to fit into the skull. Its cell structure became increasingly complex, too.

A somewhat more provocative question than the one which seems to assign priority to the chicken or the egg is this one: Which came first—the hand, the eye, or the forebrain? Hands are better investigative organs than snouts, for they can feel an object and then bring it to either eyes, nose, or mouth for closer examination. But the brain tells the hand to grasp, most characteristically in primates upon receiving a message from the eyes. Hence, among descendants of that little tree-shrew who was the ancestor of both apes and men, those had a selective advantage whose genes mutated in the direction of forming hands *or* improving vision *or* making connections in the brain which would more speedily coordinate the other two. Sooner or later a mating among subsequent descendants brought two of those genetic improvements together in one individual, and a mating in a still later generation added the third improvement—and so on, through long ages, the sum being thousands upon thousands of small improvements in total body structure and function.

It is important to remember this idea of totality. The various "improvements" weren't improvements at all unless they gave the *entire* organism an advantage. Conversely, "bad" mutations could be borne if they didn't do the entire organism too much harm. (Think of the genetic changes that must have occurred at the wrong time! A shortening of the forearms, for example, would have been a harmful mutation in early primates, who walked on all fours.)

Perhaps 30,000,000 years ago, along came a creature something like a gibbon, an unrecognizable descendant of his ancestor tree-shrew. (And why not? Millions of years lay between them.) He was much larger. He had no tail. He had binocular stereoscopic vision. And his pelvic bones had swung backward and flattened a bit, so that he could stand and run erect. Although he was basically a quadruped, his optional new posture not only freed his arms for work other than locomotion (a mutation for short arms would now be an advantage) but also put his head well above the meadow grass and brush. Therefore, he did not have to live exclusively in trees in order to be safe from ground-based enemies: from his new vantage point, and with his acute depth and distance perception, he could see them sufficiently soon to scramble back to the shelter of the forest.

By perhaps 10,000,000 years ago, nature had composed several variations on the primate theme. The monkeys had become a distinct species, and ancestral forms of modern apes and men were in existence. As a group, these latter are called anthropoids. Their pelvic bones had shortened, broadened, and tipped so that they could hold an erect posture for a considerable period of time. Their hand-eye coordination was good. Even more important, so was their mental ability to link cause and effect. They were quite capable of picking up a branch (for no reason other than curiosity), seeing a desired object in a hard-to-reach cranny, spontaneously using the branch to poke the object out, then remembering that they had done so. What they had done, of course, was to invent tool-using.

One group among the anthropoids pursued this activity no farther. By a million or two years ago (one second, give or take a fraction, on the cosmic clock), those who would become apes—today's gorillas, chimpanzees, orang-utans—had become increasingly specialized for an arboreal life. Their diet was, as it has remained, largely vegetative. Their brain capacity increased no more. As a group, these primates are called pongids.

Another group within the anthropoids, however, had adopted a quite different way of life. They are called hominids. The quality that distinguished them from the pongids was their greater competence in the use of tools. We will discuss a little later the role of technology in the development of *Homo sapiens;* let it suffice now to say that an event of primary significance to us as humans was the discovery by some tribe of hominids that stones whose edges have been chipped will cut, whereas the kind one finds smooth-polished in a riverbed will not.

It took a million or so years of physiological refinement

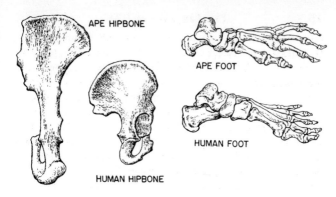

 APE HIPBONE

HUMAN HIPBONE

APE FOOT

HUMAN FOOT

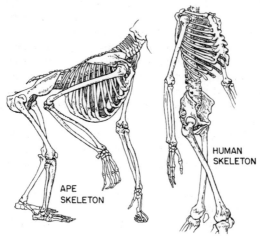

APE SKELETON

HUMAN SKELETON

Figure 17

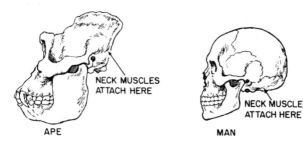

APE

NECK MUSCLES ATTACH HERE

MAN

NECK MUSCLES ATTACH HERE

Figure 18

before the descendants of those hominids could properly be called our direct ancestors (see sketches, previous page). But with the initial discovery that one can make tools, our species appeared on the evolutionary horizon. Apes can use tools, but only man can *fabricate* them.

Another important development was that some hominids became omnivorous. To be able to eat almost anything gave them a great advantage over other animals, and they tended to multiply at a greater rate. Meat is a more concentrated source of energy than fruits, nuts, or insects, and the hominids who ate it did not have to spend as much time foraging for food as their vegetarian contemporaries. Their extra leisure allowed them more time to use their hands and heads for other activities— for example, the invention of better tools, including weapons that could be used to kill the animals that were their source of meat. Parts of the head engineered for grabbing, holding, and shaking—the sharp canine teeth, the bony ridge across the eyes, the powerful musculature which linked it to jaw and backbone—all atrophied (*see Figure 18*). They were replaced by more efficient hands and arms, by the tools that were the extension of their limbs, and by a brain designed to direct the skilled use of those tools.

There is a record now, in skulls that date back almost two million years, of the transition of subman to man— of the gradual change in profile from the forward-jutting jaw, big face, and back-sloping forehead still characteristic of the pongids to the small jaw, small face, and huge forward-bulging brain of man. The increase in the size of the brain, during the years between that time and ours, was not general: it was concentrated in that part of the brain that controls movements of hand, mouth, and throat; the part that enables an individual to concentrate on a task; the part that stores memories and associations. It was this part that has given man his great dominance over his environment, his ability to guide his own affairs in a rational manner, and his unique power of speech.

Not until 50,000 to 75,000 years ago was the biological job complete, and an individual whom we would recognize as kin today—*Homo sapiens*—walked and talked and used his hands and head much as we do. He did not differ from the apes in kind (nor do we), but he differed greatly in degree—as much as our descendants, if the human line survives, may differ from us after an equivalent amount of time has elapsed. It is amusing to speculate on the behavior of *Homo super sapiens* a million years from now if it should be claimed that he is descended directly from primitive creatures like us. He may be as outraged as we were, in 1859, when it was first claimed that *we* are descended from apes.

Chapter 7

MAN'S DOUBLE INHERITANCE

The world's most advanced primates might still be man-like creatures who grunted at each other while they ate raw meat—if they hadn't learned how to put it on a spit and to swap recipes for cooking it. Which is another way of saying that what turned us into *Homo sapiens* was language, technology, and sociability.

The lower animals behave as they do because of instinct. If one passes a balsa wood model shaped like an airplane above a pen of young wildfowl which have been hatched in a laboratory, they will run and scatter—as if a hawk were flying overhead. But if you reverse the motion, so that the tail of the plane precedes the wings, the young fowl apparently see it as a long-necked goose; in any case, they are not alarmed. What do laboratory-hatched birds know of predatory hawks or harmless geese?

Instinctive behavior is the kind that is inherited, is un-modified by experience, and is performed without the animals having any idea of an action's purpose or result. Man has instincts, too—but his behavior is less controlled by them. He can alter his responses on the basis of remembered experience, can pass on to his young the fruits of such experience, and can apply knowledge gained in one situation to another situation. A spider, for example, builds her web in a shape dictated by instinct. If conditions change so that it no longer serves its purpose well, she can't modify it to suit the new situation. Man's architecture, on the other hand, attests to his ability to innovate.

Where did he get that ability?

It has been widely believed in the recent past that man developed a big brain, came down from the trees, and learned to use implements—approximately in that order; but (as suggested in the last chapter) many anthropologists today believe that the reverse is more likely. They cite the fact that the size of the brain has increased approximately threefold since creatures who were definitely *not* modern men began to make and use implements. The anthropologist L. Clark Howell has found evidence, in Spain, that members of what he calls "an extinct species of our genus" were systematically hunting and killing elephants as long ago as 500,000 years.[1] He and other anthropologists believe that the brain of modern man developed *after* and *because* his precursors took to walking upright and using implements; in other words, that it is the consequence of subman's adoption of a technological way of life.

As there was need for greater manual dexterity—for chipping a flint into a spear head, say, or for tying it onto a shaft—individuals whose genes had mutated to make their thumbs and forefingers function better were the ones who lived longer, had more children, and passed on to them the mutated genes. If a hunter managed to kill an animal that was too big for him to drag home, it was to his advantage to have brain cells that enabled him to remember where he'd cached it; and it was an even greater advantage if he could remember next year the location of the place where the hunting had been good this year. Thus the capacity of the brain grew, little by little, over thousands of years. The selective evolutionary agent was the use of tools or weapons.

And at the same time that mutations were occurring in genes controlling manual dexterity or ability to remember something, those that control the formation of the muscles and organs that make speech possible were changing, too. Whenever they helped man-in-the-making perform better in a primitive technological society, they survived.

Animals, of course, *communicate* with others of their kind; so, for that matter, does the human infant. Bees do

---

[1] Professor Howell, who is at the University of Chicago, is currently writing the official report of his findings. He is also the author of *Early Man*, in *Life* Magazine's Nature Library, an excellent, up-to-date account of the new anthropology.

a particular kind of dance to inform other bees that they have located a source of nectar. Birds and fish adopt particular postures or gestures to indicate particular intentions. Apes and monkeys alter their cries in accordance with a set series of situations which have meaning to others in their troop. But only man has evolved a system of words to symbolize objects, actions, thoughts, and the relationships between them.

It is language that makes possible the utilization by one generation of the experience of preceding generations. How would you, the elder of a tribe, inform the young ones that the rains had come at a certain time in past years and probably would again—without language? Language speeds up cooperative action and makes elaborate group activity possible. A troop of baboons can post lookouts, but only a tribe of men can dispatch lookouts from a central camp to specific, named locations. Language makes possible a man's checking the validity of his observations with someone else, the sharing of ideas about day and night, fire and water, life and death, and other mysteries of the universe.

Children babble random sounds, then learn to put those sounds together that the adults in their society obviously approve of. ("John, the baby said 'dog' today! Darling, say 'dog' for Daddy!") The next stage is a set of pat phrases, oft-repeated. Eventually a child can recombine words heard first in one construction into other constructions.

Language itself may have developed in much the same way—from random sounds descriptive of generalized situations to sounds indicative of particular things. Those sounds may have been imitative at first, but when one considers the small number of sounds that the human throat can make or the ear can discriminate, and the vast number of things that even primitive man might have wanted to talk about, one can see immediate limits to a method of communication based on growling like a bear when you're talking about a hunt or gurgling like water to suggest a trip to the river.

Another system had to be found. That system is the

same in all languages: it involves the combination of very slightly different sounds in a variety of sequences to make words whose meaning has been arbitrarily assigned to them. Say "house," "hearse," "horse." The differences in sound are slight; the differences in meaning, great. And none of those words is any more descriptive of the actual physical reality it symbolizes than any other three words would be—for example, *"casa," "carro fúnebre,"* and *"caballo."* The human brain encodes and decodes these symbols so swiftly that we moderns, the heirs of this stupendous achievement, are totally unaware of the marvels going on inside our skulls as we talk.

All this—the improved use of implements, the bigger brain, the art of language, the development of memory and reason—happened concurrently but over a long stretch of years. One gasps a bit on contemplating the exquisite timing that was necessary—not to bring us into being but just to make us *possible*. Nature must have made mistakes by the millions.

Among the problems that had to be solved before modern man could come on the scene was one that the anthropologist Sherwood L. Washburn refers to as nature's "obstetrical dilemma."[2] Here it is:

1. The use of implements gave a selective advantage to creatures who could stand erect and whose increasing brain capacity made possible ever more discriminating use of those implements.

2. But upright posture narrowed the size of the birth canal. A human infant (if born with the same degree of self-sufficiency as the newborn of other primates) couldn't be delivered because its skull would be too big to pass down the birth canal.

3. The answer to *that* was for the baby to be born "prematurely"—that is, at an earlier stage of development than an ape baby, while its head was small and pliable.

4. However, the human infant is so immature at that

[2] From "Tools and Human Evolution," *Scientific American,* September 1960.

stage of development that it can't do anything for itself. Newborn apes can crawl and climb, and hang onto the fur of the mother's back as she hunts food; but newborn humans are helpless.

5. The answer to *that* was to have the mother hold the baby in her arms. But she couldn't hold a child and gather food at the same time, could she?

6. Hence the biological change that made possible her giving birth to helpless young had to coincide with the development of a society which practiced division of labor according to sex and had developed the idea of sharing. Then the men could hunt and the women could care for the children.

Man, therefore, is also the product of his social institutions. We owe our evolution as much to our ability to develop, pass on, and modify patterns of behavior as to our physical inheritance as individuals.

Thus, we have a double inheritance.

Our *biological inheritance* comes from parent to child, through the genes; and it is basic to the other. Our *cultural inheritance* comes from the millions who have gone before us: men who organized themselves into social groups, as we do, the better to transmit accumulated wisdom to the oncoming generation. It is that wisdom which distinguishes us from the animals. From it come the arts, the law, technology, science, and religion; political and economic institutions; sentiment, morality, and consciousness of self.

Chapter 8

CIVILIZATION AND THE GROWTH OF SCIENCE

Primitive man had much to speculate about. Where does my dead father reside, he who visits me when I am asleep? How does it happen that there is ripe grain on the riverbank this year the same as last? What causes some women to give birth, and not others? It was a feat of intellect to arrive at the concept of dreams, to make a connection between time present and time past and acquire a rudimentary calendar, or to develop a sense of cause and effect sufficiently sophisticated so that the germination of seeds or the connection between the act of mating and the birth of a child could be understood.

"As first things come hardest, let us not think of such achievements as natural," warns Georgio de Santillana, the historian of science. Savage, unlettered, and full of superstition they may have been, our ancient forebears, but they were observant enough and imaginative enough to "coax fire onto the hearth, discover leverage for the spear thrower, use tension and twist to send the arrow hurtling through the air."

The earliest hominid societies killed whatever they could bash with sticks or stones and picked up whatever food was handy. This simple hunting and gathering pattern later evolved into human societies in which spears and axes were elegantly crafted, tribal hunts were organized, and systematic food-collection was practiced. Then, about 10,000 years ago, man made a great discovery: that he could domesticate animals and raise his own food.

When one grows and stores food, instead of being dependent on the chance of finding it, energy is released for activity other than food procurement. Agriculture encourages people to group in settled communities, and in due course there were enough people in any given village so there were a few non-agricultural jobs to do. A society smart enough to have figured out division of labor in the first place was only refining it with the invention of blacksmiths, bookkeepers, and priests.

The first cities—in Mesopotamia, in the fourth millennium B.C.—grew out of the agricultural way of life because it was convenient for villages to have a market place for the exchange of surplus goods. With the rise of cities, such political, social, and religious institutions as kingship, social classes, and an organized priesthood evolved. Cities became centers of invention and learning. Their existence made possible the varied human contacts that are essential to the generation of new ideas. It is worth noting that the root word of "civilization" is the Latin word for "city."

The basis of most of what we know about handling energy or matter was laid down four or five thousand years ago. The ancients who lived in the great cities along the Nile and the Euphrates used standard weights and measures, had money, kept accounts, employed geometry in land measurement and building. They invented the *idea* of writing, but it was the Phoenicians—in the second millennium B.C.—who gave us an alphabet. Earlier peoples had drawn pictures of things, but the Phoenicians substituted symbols that stood for sounds. As a nation of mariners, they also learned much about the sea, the stars, and the mathematics of navigation.

The Greeks, from the fifth century B.C. to the second century A.D. made even greater strides in scholarship. Their towering figures have cast shadows into schoolrooms ever since—especially Hippocrates and Aristotle, early in this period, and Galen and Ptolemy later.

Hippocrates was a physician. He kept such accurately observed case histories that they are a storehouse of information to this day. He set standards for the behavior of medical men and stated them so eloquently that modern physicians still pledge themselves to uphold them.

Galen, who was trained at Alexandria and practiced in Rome in the second century A.D., added to the work of Hippocrates, gathered up loose ends, and left his heirs with a complete synthesis of what had been learned up to his day of the nature of disease and the arts of healing.

Aristotle was a philosopher, a first-class naturalist, a brilliant "generalist" who brought man's knowledge of the world about him into systematic relationships. He was one of those who reveled in the beauty and elegance of the new science of mathematics,[1] and he saw in the totality of existence much evidence of design. The circle struck him as perfection itself, hence he chose it as the basic figure of an earth-centered universe. The heavens, Aristotle said, are a series of concentric crystalline spheres within which stars and planets move with uniform velocity and in eternal orbits. This perfect order of circular motion has always been and will always be: there was no Creator, there will be no Destroyer.

Ptolemy was a contemporary of Galen, and like him had been trained at Alexandria. He was a geographer and an astronomer; among his achievements was the correct measurement of the distance of the moon from the earth.

Thus, by the time of Galen's death in about A.D. 200, mankind had acquired a legacy of two great scientific[2] disciplines: mathematics and the physical sciences on the one hand, medicine and the biological sciences on the other. . . . And then, in the Western world of Europe, all inquiry into the nature of the universe ceased. Although much of importance to our cultural history occurred during the next thousand years (the rise of Christianity, for the most important example), man came out of this period knowing no more about himself and his world than the Greeks had.

By the twelfth century, however, Europe had re-established the civic order of which the fall of Rome had deprived it. The Church's spiritual and intellectual authority had been consolidated. Economic conditions had improved. And, as commerce (or war) with the Moslem Empire brought in what men called "the new learning," the West regained its heritage—the teachings of the ancient Greeks.

The brilliance with which Aristotle in particular had

---

[1] "Mathematics" once meant, simply, "learning."
[2] . . . and *"scientia"* meant "knowledge."

systematized all knowledge into a coherent and unified view of the world so overwhelmed the scholars of the Middle Ages that they spent a good two hundred years just catching up with their heritage, and feeling so inferior by comparison with the Philosopher that they hesitated to question his conclusions. True, they modified such Aristotelian thought as was in direct opposition to the teachings of Christianity; the idea, for example, that the universe had always existed was changed to allow for a precise moment of Creation. But in general they accepted Aristotle's proof that the earth is motionless and at the center of a universe whose various just-touching spheres make a continuous chain from the abode of imperfect man on earth to God and the angels in eternal perfection on high.

It was a view that still squares better with what the ordinary citizen sees or senses than what he learns at school. It is as apparent to us as to the most primitive Bushman that change is inherent in the human state and that our lives are often affected by forces beyond our control, whereas the remote and mysterious heavens do not seem to change and *do* exert an influence on the affairs of earthbound men. Even today many of us find it hard to think of lightning as a massive discharge of electricity, of the stars as moving bodies, or of ourselves as other than creatures situated halfway between a geographical Hell and Heaven.

It was a concept of the universe in which individual man was important, if only ultimately, in the matter of his eternal soul; and that's why the proposals of Copernicus and Kepler, in the sixteenth and seventeenth centuries, were so vigorously resisted. The fact that the two astronomers made the earth revolve around the sun was less important than that they destroyed earth as the core of the universe. They turned it into just one of several celestial bodies, all of them fundamentally alike; wrenched apart the chain of being that had previously linked imperfect, changeable earth to perfect, eternal Heaven; and thus destroyed many of the assumptions underlying medieval

Christian concepts of life, of death, of man's relationships to his fellows and to God.

Resistance to change is an innate trait of mankind, and a great source of stability it is, too; but curiosity is also an innate trait of mankind. A few men in each generation challenge "known facts" or put them together in new ways. Hence, the period when the wisdom of the ancient Greeks was accepted unquestioningly was followed by one in which scholars tested this wisdom against their own observations.

As sixteenth- and seventeenth-century seamen roamed ever more widely, they discovered that the ancient geographer Ptolemy was wrong in certain respects. Therefore they felt free to doubt Ptolemy's findings as an astronomer. Sixteenth- and seventeenth-century physicians discovered that Galen had indeed been right in his contention that the arteries contain blood rather than air, but Harvey in particular proved that Galen was dead wrong in other conclusions about the circulatory system.

Proof of error and acceptance of a new idea in one field of learning make it easier to challenge tradition in other fields, and eventually the whole of Renaissance Europe was in a ferment of debate about the nature of universe and man's place in the scheme of things. A few outspoken men were even saying that the peak of civilization hadn't necessarily been reached at the time of the ancient Greeks: look at the printing press, the compass, gunpowder, algebra—all recent inventions.

What Galileo had started at the beginning of the seventeenth century, Newton finished at its end, disproving once and for all Aristotle's ideas about motion and gravity; and the foundations for what has been called the Age of Reason had been laid. The Church had been unseated as the intellectual authority of Europe. A new and powerful commercial aristocracy had evolved, the arts and scholarship had become increasingly secularized, and achievements of technology were revolutionizing the economic life of nations. (The steam engine is one important example.)

This was when the idea of individual or social "progress" originated. Men abandoned the medieval belief that they are doomed sinners in a world which is gradually declining from a higher and more perfect state. They decided instead that they *had* been made in God's image, that they could improve their circumstances and direct their own destinies. Hence, contemplation of God gave way to inquiry about man and matter. Efforts to elucidate vital principles—the cosmic relationships between and among things—gave way to concern about how a specific machine or organism functioned. As a result, the old verities came tumbling down.

By the end of the eighteenth century, the French chemist Lavoisier had proved that phlogiston—"the fire element" which was thought to escape when something burned—didn't exist; that air was not an element, but a combination of oxygen and nitrogen; and that respiration in living things is a form of combustion. The British chemist Cavendish had destroyed the old notion that water is an element, and had split it into oxygen and hydrogen. The two of them, and others, had thus prepared men to accept the idea that seeming entities *may* be composed of smaller units.

Then, to the English Hooke's seventeenth-century discovery that living matter is made up of "an infinite company of small Boxes"—that is, cells—was added the eighteenth-century finding of the French scientist Bichat that all tissues of the body are basically similar, and the French Lamarck's assertion that tissues are a mass of cells. By the middle of the nineteenth century, the fact that cells had individual walls and nuclei and were the basic unit of all living things was known and accepted.

In short, from the eighteenth century onward, knowledge of the structure and function of living organisms burgeoned. (The pace of discovery is still accelerating.) Inorganic chemists, physicists, geologists, astronomers, and mathematicians also probed deep and far into the secrets of the universe and stripped many of them of their mystery.

It was not only mankind's release from the permanent perfection of an earth-centered universe that had accomplished all this; it was also an about-face on the Greeks' methods of arriving at conclusions. They had formulated general laws from "self-evident" facts, as when Aristotle deduced that the speed of an object's fall is proportional to its weight. (It is self-evident that stones fall faster than feathers.) But, beginning with Galileo, scientists did just the reverse: they made observations, and on the basis of the observations formulated general laws. (Having checked the fall of various objects, Galileo showed that except for differences in resistance to air they all fall at the same rate.) This insistence that one cannot generalize except from observation is the cornerstone of modern science.

A corollary is that science provides no "ultimate" truth. Just as no discovery is accepted until a second investigator repeats the observations of the first and confirms his conclusions, so both investigators realize that future observations may cause amendments to the original work. Today it is the *non*-scientist, expressing mankind's common yearning for certainties, who attributes a sense of finality to discoveries in science. Scientists know—often to their despair as human beings—that science is an endless opening of sealed boxes which turn out to have more sealed boxes inside. The more one learns, the more there *is* to learn. There is never a last word.

In taking this quick backward glance across billions of years of time, we have described as milestones of life the evolution of genes themselves, of multicellular organisms, of creatures with central nervous systems, of thinking and talking men—and, finally, of the human culture that enabled us to ask "why?", search for the answers, and pass them on to our children. Together, they have made us as a species what we are today.

The rest of this book will consider in detail just one question of the many that modern man seeks to answer: Why is it that we humans, although general in kind, are unique as individuals?

Chapter 9

THE MENDELIAN LAWS

You've seen him in the movies: the scientist who is infallible, insensitive, and coldly objective—little more than an animated computer in a white lab coat. He takes measurements and records results as if the collection of data were his sole object in life; and if a meaningful pattern emerges it comes as a blinding surprise. The assumption is that if one gathers enough facts about something, the relationships between those facts will spontaneously reveal themselves.

Nonsense.

In the real world of science, the investigator almost always knows what he's looking for before he starts. His observations are usually undertaken to prove the validity of an idea, and his emotions are as deeply engaged as those of a businessman planning a sales campaign, a general mapping out strategy, or a hunter stalking big game.

It's true that scientists strive for objectivity; what's more, they achieve it more often than other men. But they are no more capable than other men of maintaining absolute neutrality toward the outcome of their work. Nor could *you,* if you were testing an original hypothesis that you believed to be both unique and imaginative. Who among us would not like to make a successful thrust into the unknown, to find a missing link, to break a code?

Scientists are more curious than most of their fellows, more intelligent than many, and the best of them are as creative as the best composers, poets, or painters. But they are equally human. Thus they are liable to error, subject to luck, and affected by the political or emotional climate of their times in much the same way as anyone else is.

The myth of infallibility evaporates when one thinks of the number of great ideas in science whose originators were correct only in general but wrong in detail. Dalton, for example, gets credit for the atomic theory as we know it today—yet his formulas for figuring atomic weights were basically incorrect. Copernicus was mistaken in the particulars of his sun-centered universe; it doesn't explain the movements of the planets any better than Ptolemy's earth-centered universe did. Newton amended Kepler; and even Newton's laws of physics have been modified (although not in ways important to the layman) by Einstein.

It may be no easier for a scientist to challenge the prevailing thought of his time than for any other man. Witness Darwin's excessive caution in avoiding mention of *human* evolution when he wrote *Origin of Species*. He realized the implications of his work, and anticipated the storm of public protest.

It's even harder for a scientist to defend an opinion that is unpopular among other scientists. The Swedish chemist Arrhenius, for example, was almost denied his Ph.D. because of wild ideas expressed in his thesis about the existence of particles he called "ions"; and although there is a Cinderella twist to his story—nineteen years later, after electrons had been discovered, he was awarded a Nobel prize for the same research that had nearly lost him his degree—there are numerous examples of other scientists who went to their graves with *their* wild ideas unnoticed or unvalidated. One such was the English physician Garrod, the forgotten man of biochemistry. He suggested that genes control chemical reactions by the use of enzymes, but his theories fitted neither into the context of scientific thought of his time nor into an established scientific discipline, and neither chemists nor biologists took proper note of them.

Luck, too, has played as much of a role in scientific discovery as in any other human endeavor. The German astronomer Kepler, for example, made two mistakes in simple arithmetic in calculating the orbit of Mars; but by a fantastic coincidence they canceled each other, and he got the right answer. Pasteur demonstrated, by sterilizing organic cultures in sealed flasks, that life does not generate spontaneously from air; but it was lucky that he happened to use an easy-to-kill yeast and not the hay bacillus that another investigator had chosen for the same experiment. We know now that hay bacillus is heat-resistant and grows even after boiling. If Pasteur had used it, his "proof" would have been long a-coming, despite the correctness of his basic idea.

And if the history of science is a very human document, then Gregor Mendel, the father of modern genetics, is a very human scientist. Like Dalton, his conclusions were correct only in general, wrong in detail. Like Arrhenius, he postulated the existence of particles for which there was no experimental evidence—except his; indeed, scientists weren't even prepared for the idea that such particles might exist. Like Garrod, and for the same reasons, he was ignored in his own time. Like Pasteur, he was incredibly lucky in his choice of research material. And like many an investigator before and after his time, his observations reveal the very human tendency to weight the scales in one's own favor, if only subconsciously.

Mendel, an Augustinian monk, had had some training in mathematics and the natural sciences. In addition, he was the son of a farmer, knew the soil, and had a green thumb. Plant hybridization interested him, and he began to read the professional literature. There were many puzzling problems. Crosses between certain species regularly yielded many hybrids with identical traits, for instance; but look what happened when you crossed the hybrids—all kinds of strange new combinations of traits cropped up. The principle of inheritance, if there *was* one, was elusive.

Mendel's basic (and original) idea was that there might be simple mathematical relationships among the character-istic forms of plants in different generations of hybrids. He decided, therefore, to establish some experimental plots in the monastery garden at Brünn, and there raise a number of varieties of peas,[1] hybridize them, count and classify the offspring of each generation, and see whether any mathe-matical ratios were involved.

Animal and plant breeding had been practiced from

[1] *Not* sweet peas, as is widely believed. The common garden pea, the kind you eat, was his research material.

the days of the ancient Egyptians, and it was so apparent that children "take after" their parents and that traits "run in families" that the *fact* of inheritance was indisputable. But nobody knew the mechanism. Discoveries identifying the cell as the fundamental unit of life had not been pulled together in any orderly way until the German scientists Schwann and Schleiden did it in 1839, and about all that anyone knew for sure in the early years of the nineteenth century was that sperm cells fertilized egg cells. No one knew what went on inside either.

The seventeenth-century idea that sperm contained a "manikin" (a complete but miniature human being) had gone by the boards; and in 1854, when Mendel began his study of inheritance, the prevailing theory was that an "essence" from each vital organ of the parents' bodies somehow blended to create a new individual. (The belief that a baby gets half its blood from its father and half from its mother is memorialized by such phrases as "blood will tell.") Although it had occurred to various scientists that discrete particles, each affecting different traits, might be passed on from generation to generation, there was no experimental proof. Nor had anyone taken the possibility seriously enough to attempt to prove it.

Mendel had noted that in some varieties of peas, the unripe pods were green while in others they were yellow. Some varieties grew tall, others were dwarf types. Still other pairs of clearly distinct characteristics in different varieties of peas had to do with position of flowers (distributed along the stem or clustered at the top), the form of ripe pods (puffed out or indented), the color of the seed coats (white or gray), the color of the ripe seeds (green or yellow), and the form of the ripe seeds (smooth or wrinkled). Mendel chose these seven paired characteristics to keep tabs on.

He began with seed that other growers had certified as "pure" (that is, plants grown from it, if self-fertilized, faithfully duplicated the traits of the parental stock)— but just to make sure, he raised plants from it and harvested a crop. Then, by artificial pollination, he crossed varieties in different combinations. The result, for each of the seven paired traits he had chosen to study, was the same: *all* individuals in the first generation took after one parent. It was as if the other parent had had no influence whatever on the result.

Take the cross between smooth and wrinkled peas as an example (*Figure 19*). All the seeds (which are in reality first-generation plants) were smooth. Why? Why weren't there some wrinkled ones, too? Maybe the two traits combined in such a way that one lost its identity, was absorbed by the other; in effect was destroyed. That would certainly be a reasonable conclusion on the basis of this first-generation evidence. But Mendel intended to draw no conclusions until he had followed the various traits in peas through several generations.

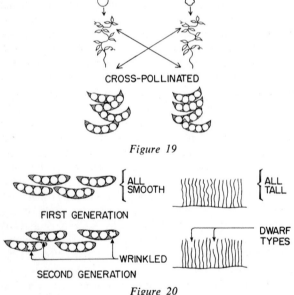

CROSS-POLLINATED

Figure 19

ALL SMOOTH

ALL TALL

FIRST GENERATION

DWARF TYPES

WRINKLED

SECOND GENERATION

Figure 20

He cross-pollinated only to produce the first-generation hybrids. Thereafter—for example, when the first-generation hybrid seeds became plants—they would be allowed to self-pollinate, as is natural for pea plants. In this process, the eggs of a given flower are fertilized by the sperm carried in the pollen of that same flower. And when the second-generation seeds were produced on hybrid plants in this way, Mendel observed that a strange thing had happened. The "lost" traits began to show up! (*See Figure 20.*) An occasional *wrinkled* pea lay alongside the prevailing smooth ones. When the original cross had been between varieties with yellow and green seeds, a few *green* pea seeds were now scattered among the prevailing yellow ones. For characters that show only in mature plants—such as height, position, or color of flowers—the second-generation seeds produced some plants like one of the original "pure" parents, some like the other parent.

Was there a mathematical ratio? Mendel harvested a large number of pods, and in the smooth/wrinkled group he found about 5400 smooth and about 1800 wrinkled seeds. Among those whose original ancestors had been yellow- and green-seeded, he found both types in the second generation in a ratio of about three yellow to one green—approximately 6000 to 2000 in one set of data he recorded. And in the five other paired characteristics he was studying, results were the same: in each case, about 25 per cent of the second-generation plants showed the traits that had appeared to "vanish" in the preceding generation.

Then one trait had *not* absorbed or destroyed the other. One trait must simply have been more "forceful" than the other. The determinants of the two traits had kept their separate identities—except that the weaker one had been submerged, its effect masked. Mendel called the more forceful trait the "dominant" one; the less forceful, the "recessive" one. He expressed the distinction by using capital letters to indicate dominants and lower-case letters to indicate recessives.

Here is the kind of exercise he must have done as he was figuring out the significance of what he had found:

In the cells that give rise to sperm-carrying pollen and also in the cells that produce eggs, let A stand for the determinant for smoothness and a for its alternate, the determinant for wrinkledness. An egg cell has an equal chance of getting *A* or *a,* and the same is true for sperm cells. The primary ratio in such cells is therefore 1*A* to 1*a.* One or the other will come together in each pairing that brings the next generation into being.

Consider next—as Mendel was having to consider— the possibility that each of the two determinants for a given pair of traits were present as discrete entities (even if invisible) in the cells of the first-generation plants. There would be four ways in which these traits could combine in producing the second-generation offspring. What has since Mendel's day come to be called a "checkerboard" diagram graphically indicates (*see Figure 21*) the four combinations.

Figure 22 repeats the checkerboard, this time with shading overlying spaces holding dominant *A*'s. All peas of this type would be smooth. Only peas of the *aa* type would be wrinkled. The second-generation ratio, then, would be 3*A* to 1*a*—three-fourths of the progeny smooth, one-fourth wrinkled. This squared very nicely with Mendel's observations upon counting his second-generation crop of pea seeds, 75 per cent of which were smooth and 25 per cent wrinkled.

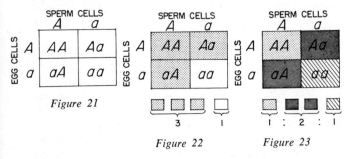

Figure 21

Figure 22

Figure 23

But 3:1 is not an accurate description of their *inherent constitution;* it is descriptive only of their outward appearance. As you see in *Figure 23,* one-fourth of the offspring would be pure for the dominant trait (*AA*—smoothness), one-fourth would be pure for the recessive trait (*aa*—wrinkledness), and one-half would be hybrid mixtures of *A* and *a*. The correct ratio, then, is 1*AA* to 2 *Aa* to 1*aa*.

The same principle is illustrated by tossing two coins simultaneously (*see Figure 24*). There is only one combination that will result in. two heads, and only one combination that will result in two tails, but there are two combinations that will result in a heads-and-tails throw:

HEADS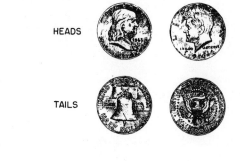

TAILS

  HEADS AND TAILS

Figure 24

The ratio, here too, is 1:2:1.

Once Mendel had figured out these mathematical relationships in his first- and second-generation seeds, he knew what he was looking for in subsequent plantings.

He planted the second-generation seeds—the generation, remember, in which 25 per cent of the peas had made a wrinkled comeback; and in the third generation, these wrinkled peas, the "recessives," bred true to type. Furthermore, they did so in all the following years that Mendel planted their descendants.

Of those in the second generation that carried the "dominant" trait—the 75 per cent that looked smooth— only one in three (on the average) bred true to type, and

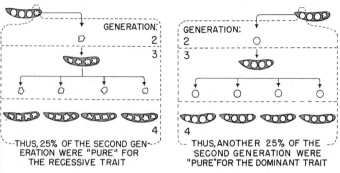

Figure 25

THUS, 25% OF THE SECOND GENERATION WERE "PURE" FOR THE RECESSIVE TRAIT

Figure 26

THUS, ANOTHER 25% OF THE SECOND GENERATION WERE "PURE" FOR THE DOMINANT TRAIT

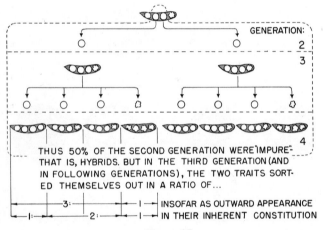

THUS 50% OF THE SECOND GENERATION WERE "IMPURE"—THAT IS, HYBRIDS. BUT IN THE THIRD GENERATION (AND IN FOLLOWING GENERATIONS), THE TWO TRAITS SORTED THEMSELVES OUT IN A RATIO OF...

3 : 1 → INSOFAR AS OUTWARD APPEARANCE

1 : 2 : 1 → IN THEIR INHERENT CONSTITUTION

Figure 27

continued thereafter to do so. The diagrams at the top of this page show these "pure" lines.

And, on the average, two out of the three that looked smooth did *not* breed true to type, but repeated the pattern of the second generation (*see Figure 27*).

Indeed, inheritance *did* follow an orderly rule. Given a pair of separate and distinct particles to start with, the way in which they would be passed along was statistically predictable.

The logical next question was: Would the same results occur if *two* different traits were crossed? (Let *Aa* stand for smoothness-wrinkledness and *Bb* stand for yellowness-greenness.) The first-generation hybrid plants would then be symbolized as *Aa Bb,* and the eggs of such a plant would be of four kinds: *AB, Ab, aB,* and *ab.* All possible combinations would appear with equal frequency. Perhaps this is a good place to use the examples of coin tossing again, this time a half-dollar and a quarter, flipped at random. As you see in *Figure 28,* four combinations are possible:

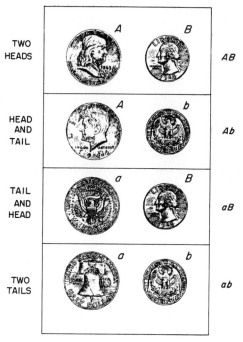

TWO HEADS	*A* *B*	*AB*
HEAD AND TAIL	*A* *b*	*Ab*
TAIL AND HEAD	*a* *B*	*aB*
TWO TAILS	*a* *b*	*ab*

Figure 28

Now, if eggs of the four kinds are fertilized at random by sperms of the same four kinds, the results can be shown by the checkerboard diagram of sixteen squares in *Figure 29.*

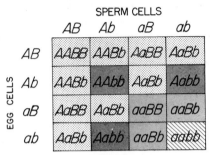

Figure 29

Count the squares that contain either *A*'s or *B*'s: there are nine of them, and the resultant peas should be smooth and yellow (dominant traits).

Count the squares that contain either *A*'s or *B*'s. There are three of each. Those with *A*'s should express themselves in the crop as smooth green peas; those with *B*'s as wrinkled and yellow.

There remains one square with no capital letters. Peas of this character should be wrinkled and green (recessive traits).

The ratio, as you see, is no longer 1:2:1 but

And how did this paperwork square with the results of a harvested pea crop when Mendel crossed smooth yellow peas with plants yielding wrinkled greens and then raised *their* offspring? Out of 556 ripe peas, he got

Smooth yellow   Smooth green   Wrinkled yellow   Wrinkled green

Smooth yellow	Smooth green	Wrinkled yellow	Wrinkled green
315	108	101	32

Approximately 9:3:3:1

The inevitable next question, of course, was: Would field tests confirm the statistical prediction of what would happen if one were to cross *three* characters? A first-generation hybrid *Aa Bb Cc* should produce a second-generation ratio of 27:9:9:3:9:3:3:1. We'll skip the checkerboard this time, because of its formidable size and complexity[2] but when Mendel crossed hybrid peas that were smooth (*A*), yellow (*B*), and had grayish seed coats (*C*) with plants bearing peas that were wrinkled (*a*), green (*b*), and whose seed coats were white (*c*), his harvest tally of variations added up to a ratio of 27:9:9:3:9:3:3:1!

With these and other results that supported his hypothesis, his case was complete. He had grown and harvested peas for twelve years, had kept meticulous records, and now he thought he had something worth talking about. So, in 1865, he appeared before the Brünn Society for the Study of Natural Science, read a report of his research, and postulated what have since come to be called the Mendelian laws:

1. Inheritance is based on pairs of particulate units, each of which determines specific traits. (He called them "elements"; we call them "genes.") Of each pair, offspring receive *one or the other* from each parent.

2. Of each pair of elements acquired by the offspring, one is dominant and the other is recessive. (Mendel called them "antagonistic factors"; we call the two versions of each trait its "alleles.") When both parents contribute a dominant element or when both parents contribute a recessive element (*AA* or *aa*), the individual will be "pure" for that trait. If the parent contributes one dominant and one recessive (*Aa* or *aA*), the individual will be hybrid, but will look the same as the pure dominant.

3. Since these paired elements, whether dominant or recessive, are capable of separating, reappearing in their original form, and pairing differently in later unions, they are obviously not contaminated or altered in any way in the course of their passage from individual to individual.

---

[2] If you want to check on Mendel's math and at the same time show yourself how many different individuals can result from just *three* paired traits, draw a checkerboard with 64 squares and place the following symbols for egg or sperm cells: *ABC, ABc, AbC, Abc, aBC, aBc, abC, abc*. One begins to see, with this exercise, why no human being—whose cells contain not three but thousands of traits—is ever like another human being (unless he has an identical twin).

4. If two or more pairs of elements are hybrid in a single plant—*Aa* and *Bb,* say—they assort independently in the formation of eggs and sperm; that is, giving *AB, Ab, aB,* and *ab.* (This is the law of independent segregation.)

Members of the Society listened politely to Mendel, but insofar as anybody knows asked few questions and engaged in little discussion. It may even be that they sat in embarrassed silence as he proceeded, a suspicion slowly growing that a nice fellow had somehow gotten way off the track.

Mendel's assertion that separate and distinct "elements" of inheritance must exist, despite the fact that he couldn't produce any, was close to asking the Society to accept something on faith. Scientists resist accepting things on faith. There was no evidence for Mendel's hypothesis other than his computations; and his wildly unconventional application of algebra to botany made it difficult for his listeners to understand that those computations *were* the evidence.

Mendel was a careful worker, no doubt about that. And one certainly wouldn't presume to doubt the honesty of a monk. But he'd been raising those peas of his for a long time, and with such single-minded devotion that he might have developed some odd ideas about the implications of his work. Remember, too, that he was little more than a horticultural hobbyist, however dedicated. He lacked a degree, had no University connection, had no previously published research to give him a reputation. Now, if Pasteur had advanced the idea, or Darwin . . .

Anyway, who *really* expects the boy next door to grow up to be President? Surely the gentlemen of the Brünn Society can be forgiven for failing to realize that their modest neighbor had made a brilliant discovery about the fundamental nature of life. They printed his paper in their *Proceedings*—and remembered it as an oddity, if they remembered it at all.

Chapter 10

MENDEL MODIFIED

Two years after Mendel presented his paper in Brünn, he was named Abbot of his monastery. Thereafter he became too busy with civic and administrative duties—he had a long wrangle with the Austrian government over monastery taxes, for example—to do more than putter in the garden.

He had written to Karl von Nägeli, a distinguished hybridizer of the time, and had enclosed a reprint of his paper on peas. But Nägeli was as unable as members of the Brünn Society (and with less reason) to appreciate the significance of Mendel's work. He sent off a damning-with-faint-praise acknowledgment that said, in effect, "Your work shows a certain promise"; and suggested that Mendel test his theory further by using Nägeli's favorite research material, the hawkweed. Nägeli wasn't doing very well with it, and neither did Mendel. The plant was an unfortunate choice for someone interested in principles of heredity, because it happens to reproduce in a highly unusual way.

Later, Mendel also tried to study inheritance in bees. They were a bad choice, too. Mendel undoubtedly died without knowing that his findings on peas *had* illuminated a well-nigh universal pattern. Luck had simply gone against him in his subsequent choices.[1]

Mendel's luck had gone the other way, however, in his initial choice of which particular traits in peas to study. Here's why:

We now know that groups of genes (which are carried

[1] Hawkweed sets what appears to be seed, but the seeds are produced asexually. In bees, the males develop from unfertilized eggs. In neither case are the genes of two parents recombined in the offspring in the simple manner described by Mendel.

in a number of bodies called chromosomes) do not always act independently. Often they are linked, their effect being to transmit a "package" of traits. If, for example, an allele controlling surface texture of peas were completely linked to an allele controlling pea color, the two—acting as a unit—would have made Mendel's second-generation ratios come out $3:0:0:1$ or $2:1:1:0$, instead of the $9:3:3:1$ he had postulated upon assuming that the units of heredity are separate and independently acting.

Knowing nothing about chromosomes or genes, let alone the phenomenon of linkage, Mendel might well have decided that his hypothesis was wrong—and very possibly he would have quit. He was spared this fate because, out of all the possible traits in peas which he might have picked for study, he happened to choose seven traits *each of which is controlled from a different chromosome.* (The probability of anyone's making such a happy choice, in random picks, is only about 1 in 163!) Whether each of the particular traits he was studying was in fact linked to other traits made no difference, since he was following only one in each group. Because of Mendel's good luck in this matter, linkage did not confuse his results; and each trait *did* segregate independently.

It has also been discovered since Mendel's day that allelic genes sometimes (although very rarely) exchange corresponding parts. The changes brought about by such recombination are permanent and inheritable, hence one can no longer say that genes are *indivisible* particulate units or that they are never "contaminated or altered . . . in the course of their passage from individual to individual."

(In later chapters of this book, we'll go into greater detail about these modifications of Mendelian law.)

An additional discovery since Mendel did his pioneer work is that dominance and recessiveness are not as complete as he thought they were. For example, if *Aa* represents the gene for eye color—*A* being brown and *a* being blue—the Mendelian laws would have it that an *Aa* individual has eyes as dark as an *AA* individual. We know now that this is unlikely. There are *degrees* of dominance and recessiveness.

In addition, it is now obvious that many traits are the result of multi-gene action.

Skin color is a good example of these last two points. The specific number of genes at work, or the "strength" of each is not even now precisely known, but this much is clear:

All skin, whatever its color, gets that way because of variations in pigmentation in the five overlaid layers of the epidermis. The basic pigment in human skin is brown. The red of blood cells in the layer just below the skin adds a pink note. And the depth of the numerous layers through which the eye is seeing adds a blue tone.[2] In sum, whether you have the "white" skin of the Caucasoid or the "black" skin of the Congoid Negro (to choose the two extremes), it is simply a result of color intensification of the sort that occurs when one overlays successive panes of gray glass. If the glass is very pale to start with (or if pigment granules are scattered lightly in each layer), the final tone will be light. But if the glass is dark to start with (that is, if pigment granules are heavily concentrated in each layer), the final product will be dark—as shown in *Figure 30*.

Figure 30

Now, what is the gene pattern that controls the making and distribution of pigment?

At least two major genes are involved. These genes— call them *A* and *B*—are thought to have equal effect.

---

[2] Some people believe that there is a distinctly fourth color— yellow; but many others believe that Mongoloid skin is only another variation on the brown-red-blue spectrum, the yellow-brown cast being the result of differences in structure or in depth of skin layer which carries the most pigment.

(Like a pair of tennis players, *A* and *B* may do different things—but they are equally important to the game.) Each of those genes has an allele but is not fully dominant to it. (Using the analogy of the tennis game again—a doubles match, this time—it isn't as if one partner of each pair were champion quality and the other a near-dud. Rather, one player of each pair is excellent and the other is merely good.) Instead of expressing such a relationship between alleles as *Aa* and *Bb*—which indicates complete dominance and complete recessiveness—one might do it by using boldface and lightface capitals, so: **AA**BB. Thus, the end result of two genes working in tandem and of two alleles whose effect is not blotted out by the dominant partners is to get four units of inheritance that make their presence felt in the finished product.

An example of how this works appears in skin color of offspring resulting from an interracial marriage. The genes of the white parent would be AABB and those of the Negro parent would be **AABB.** Eggs and sperm would be AB or **AB,** hence all offspring would be **AA**BB—and intermediate in skin color. Medium brown.

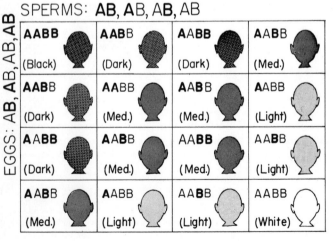

Figure 31

Suppose then that two such medium brown individuals were to marry? Let's make them a statistically perfect—rather than a real—family, and produce the sixteen children necessary to indicate all the possibilities of skin color that could result from such a union. (*See Figure 31.*)

The distribution would follow Mendelian laws in that there would be nine offspring with both **A**'s and **B**'s: three with **A**'s; three with **B**'s; and one with nothing but A's and B's. But because the dominants don't blanket out their alleles, actual skin color would correspond to the particular combination of the four alleles in each cell—as follows:

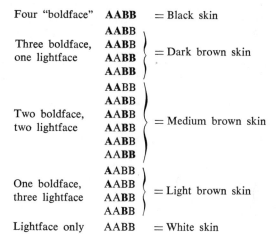

Four "boldface"	**AABB**	= Black skin
Three boldface, one lightface	**AAB**B **A**A**BB** A**ABB** **AABB**	} = Dark brown skin
Two boldface, two lightface	**AA**BB **A**AB**B** **A**A**B**B A**A**B**B** A**AB**B AA**BB**	} = Medium brown skin
One boldface, three lightface	**A**ABB A**A**BB AAB**B** AA**B**B	} = Light brown skin
Lightface only	AABB	= White skin

From the above you can see that it is impossible for any of the offspring, if subsequently mated to a white spouse, to produce a child as dark as the original dark grandparent. As the American geneticist Curt Stern has pointed out, there are no known and authenticated exceptions to this generalization, hearsay notwithstanding. So ignore those rumors you hear from time to time about a white-skinned couple who are alleged to have produced a black-skinned child because one of the parents has "hidden Negro blood."

On the other hand, as the chart indicates, a couple

of light-skinned Negroes may well produce a child who is darker than they.

In Great Britain, a number of species of moths have evolved right under the eyes of nineteenth- and twentieth-century scientists. These moths are normally light-colored, which makes them highly visible against soot-darkened buildings or trees in the industrial areas of the British Isles. This high visibility makes them easy prey for birds with a taste for moths, and they have well-nigh vanished from their original habitat. Although the light-colored species still exist in the countryside, a dark-colored variant now inhabits the cities.

These "industrial moths" have been much studied—and two facts with possible application to man have emerged:

1. Although all species have acquired additional pigmentation, it is not the same genes in every species that have mutated. The same may be true for man. In other words, if the dark skin of Congoid Negroes is due to genes **A** and **B,** it is possible that the dark skin of Caucasoids (as found in India) is due to other genes—**C** and **D,** say.

2. The fact that the industrial moths developed pigment because it gave them an advantage in their particular environment suggests that skin color variations in humans may have occurred for the same reason. Here's why:

Pigment screens out ultraviolet light—some of which is necessary, since it plays a role in the synthesis of vitamin D; but an excess can be harmful. For example, an amount of UV light that is not damaging to normal individuals can induce pre-cancerous conditions in albinos, whose skin is completely unpigmented. It is reasonable, therefore, to believe that evolutionary forces would have selected dark skin in the tropics, where the sun's rays strike the earth less obliquely than at the poles and where high temperatures induce humans to expose more of the body. The reverse would have been true in northern climes, where there is less sunlight from which to absorb ultraviolet radiation and where lower temperatures encourage people to bundle up.

As we said earlier, much remains to be found out about pigmentation in man. It is possible that there are more than two major genes involved. The ones known may turn out *not* to be of equal effect or near-equal dominance. (Instead of **AABB**, it might be necessary a few years hence to write **AABb**, to indicate that one of the two kinds of genes is more important than the other. Or there may be a greater degree of dominance than is now believed to be the case, in which event Mendel's *AaBb* convention *would* be accurate.) As when he started it all, the basic principles are clear but the details have to be worked out.

It is important to keep in mind, however, that there are thousands of traits that are inherited in *exactly* the fashion that Mendel described.

An example in humans? Let's take the inheritance of curly versus straight hair. We'll start with Susan, who has curly hair. So has everyone in her mother's family. However, since everyone in her father's family has straight hair, Susan must be a hybrid and her curly hair due to the dominance of the allele for this hair form over the allele for straight hair. Susan is married to Bill, whose hair is as curly as hers. But Bill is an orphan, with no knowledge of what his parents looked like. Bill and Susan have four children, of whom Mary, Joe, and Nancy have curly hair and one of whom, Jean, has straight hair. What, then, is Bill's genetic constitution for this trait? (*See Figure 32, next page.*)

Explanation: Each child had a 50–50 chance of getting either the allele for curly hair or the allele for straight hair from Susan. If Bill were "pure" for curly hair, each child would have received a dominant allele from him; and each child would have curly hair. But since Jean turned up with straight hair, Bill's genetic constitution for hair form must be the same as his wife's. He's a hybrid, too. He must have had parents who passed on to him both alleles for this trait.

In real life, the only child for whom one could make an exact prediction is Jean. She is "pure" for straight hair, and will pass on alleles for straight hair to her

SUSAN   BILL

MARY   JOE   NANCY   JEAN

Figure 32

BILL

SUSAN

| | MARY | JOE |
| NANCY | JEAN |

Figure 33

offspring. It would be impossible to tell by looking at them whether Mary, Joe, and Nancy are "pure" or hybrid. But, as in the earlier example on skin color, let's turn Bill and Susan and the children into a statistical family and put them into a checkerboard diagram as shown in *Figure 33*. (Incidentally, it is now genes rather than individuals that are represented.)

Mary is assumed to be "pure" for curly hair and will pass on only alleles for curly hair to her children. Joe and Nancy are hybrid, and will pass on alleles for curly *or* straight hair, just as their parents did to them—all in accordance with Mendelian rules.

There is a final footnote to Mendel's work. The ratios he reported as resulting from random sampling are too close to "ideal" to have been arrived at with the cold objectivity that fable ascribes to scientists. The statistician R. A. Fisher has calculated that if one were to repeat Mendel's total series of experiments in the same manner that he did, one would have a negligible chance of getting as close a fit as Mendel reported.

This does not mean that he was dishonest. It suggests only that he was human. He did not understand statistics and the theory of sampling well, and was no doubt biased in favor of his hypothesis. An intuitive feeling for relationships and results that make sense is as important in science as in any other endeavor: Mendel may simply have stopped counting peas when the results "seemed right."

People who plot measurements that fall on a smooth curve are familiar with this temptation. If one suddenly finds a measurement that doesn't fit well, the natural assumption is that it is wrong. If one repeats the measurement and the fit is good, the natural assumption is that the second measurement is the correct one. Now, the second measurement very well *may* be the correct one, but this is not precisely an objective way of doing an experiment.

Proper sampling procedure, in a genetic experiment such as Mendel undertook, would require that one count

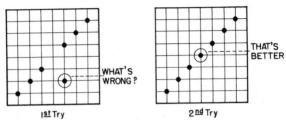

all members of a population, or at least stop at a pre-determined point. It seems probable that Mendel stopped counting whenever he approached the ratio he was looking for, but continued to count whenever the fit wasn't as good as he had hoped it might be. If so, it's a good thing that he did: in grand design, his work was basically correct.

Despite subsequent modification of Mendel's laws of inheritance, and discovery that his observations were "too good" to be accepted at face value, his was a brilliant achievement of creative intellect. He not only had an original idea and tested its validity with thoroughness that remains an example to modern scientists, but in addition he was astute enough to figure out what his data *meant*. In so doing, he provided the key that would open the door to the science of genetics.

Chapter 11

INSIDE THE CELL

Why does a clock tick? What makes it run down? These questions are not too difficult to answer, for one removes the back of the clock and watches the works; or takes the mechanism apart and examines it.

A question not so easily answered is: What makes a living organism grow? If you take it apart, you not only stop the process of growth but also prevent its resumption. Furthermore—and despite the fact that much can be learned by observing the degree of development at any given stage of an arrested life cycle—you haven't learned what you want to know unless the dynamic principle of growth is visible to the human eye.

One of the *larger* cells in the human body is the ovum, or egg cell—and, at 1/200th of an inch in diameter, it is barely visible to the naked eye. Most other cells in our bodies are smaller. For a very tiny example, the head of a sperm cell is only 1/5000th of an inch long; the scientific writer Amram Scheinfeld[1] remarks that the number of sperm needed to father all the people in the world today could be comfortably housed in a teaspoon.

Most cells of living organisms other than humans also range in size from barely visible to absolutely invisible. That's why—although it was known early in the nineteenth century that the cell is an exceedingly important unit of growth—knowledge of the structure and working of cells was dependent on the development of high-power microscopes.

The nineteenth century was into its third decade before scientists had established that most living organisms can be reduced at some stage to a single cell. In animals

[1] In *Your Heredity and Environment* (Philadelphia: J. B. Lippincott Company, 1965).

the process of development of a new individual begins with the fertilization of an egg cell by a sperm cell, which then begins a series of divisions. The first cell divides into two, the two into four, the four into eight, and so on, in geometric progression. Eventually, if that initial cell was a fertilized human egg, the result is a mature man or woman whose body contains billions of cells.

There is a stately rhythm to the sequences of cell division. The initial emphasis is on numerical increase—that is, on the production of daughter cells through successive divisions. In kind, all cells seem to be much alike at first, but at some predetermined stage in the early life of the embryo they begin to specialize, and become bone cells, muscle cells, nerve cells, and so on. From that time onward, they divide and duplicate at different rates. What is the signal? How does a cell "know" what its specialty should be?

In animals, for example, a band of cells lies along an epidermal area covering the backbone that is called the neural crest. At a certain time in early development, these cells begin to migrate. They move down and around the curled-up body of the embryo as water drains off a rounded rock. A certain amount of time later, the migration of these particular cells comes to an end, they settle down, and from then on they specialize. They make the pigment that colors skin, fur, or feathers. If they halt before their pilgrimage has carried them wholly around the body of the animal, or to its extremities—points farthest from the neural crest—the animal will not make pigment in those areas. This is the explanation of white blazes on a horse's forehead, a dog's belly, a kitten's paws.

What causes identical twins? They begin as one egg fertilized by one sperm, a cell which doubles in the normal way—but then for some reason develops into two individuals. If this happens very early, before any of the cells have specialized, the twins will be faithful duplicates of each other. If the split comes a little later, when that single embryo has begun to differentiate into a right and a left side, one twin will in many respects be the "mirror image" of the other. And if the split isn't a clean one, the parts of the developing embryo that are separate will go ahead and develop separately, whereas the part that is still fused will develop as a unit—and the tragic birth of Siamese twins will result.

What triggers activity such as we have been describing? What stops it? For that matter, how does any living thing sense that enough cells have been produced to make it an adult organism? The answers to these questions aren't known yet. But they had been posed by the middle years of the last century; much information was being gathered about the stages of growth in living organisms; and the first probes into the interior of the cell were being made.

It was known that the cell consists of a gelatinous substance—now called cytoplasm—which surrounds an inner sphere that its discoverer, the Scottish botanist Robert Brown, had named the nucleus. The importance of this body was suspected, because when embryologists interfered with normally dividing cells (the eggs of marine animals were favorites for this kind of research), the cells had enormous capacity for continued growth—*unless* the nucleus had been damaged. This central sphere, then, must be necessary for the development of the new individual that results from a fertilized egg. Perhaps by controlling the process?

Among those who had great influence was the German zoologist August Weismann. He was responsible for the concept of "germ plasm," which holds that specific parts of the egg cell or the early embryo are destined to become certain parts of the developing organism—some the eyes, others the lungs, and so on. He used the analogy of a mosaic, saying that each "chip" in the germ plasm was passed on at an appropriate time in embryonic development to serve as the model for a specific part of the new individual.

It was an appealing and logical idea, and not until very late in the century did investigators show that in some cases whole individuals (tadpoles, for instance) develop from a fertilized egg even if part of it is destroyed after it has begun to divide and duplicate itself. If Weismann's mosaic theory had been true in such cases, cutting off a part of the dividing cell should have eliminated a particular part of the mature organism. However, other parts of Weismann's germ plasm theory were quite correct; we'll come to them shortly.

But investigators of a hundred years ago couldn't progress beyond establishing that the nucleus is important to cell growth—because the cell is transparent. Even with a microscope, it was hard to distinguish one substructure from another, and whatever bodies in addition to the nucleus there might be inside that tiny bit of living matter remained a mystery.

Meanwhile, the Industrial Revolution was in full swing, and chemists were learning how to synthesize a good many materials previously obtainable only in nature. Awareness that they *could* do so was the result of the quite accidental accomplishment of the German chemist Friedrich Wöhler, in 1828. He made urea—an organic compound—in the course of heating an inorganic compound called ammonium cyanate. Later, the French chemist Pierre Berthelot made ethyl alcohol from coal, air, and water; and even managed to create a few substances that didn't occur naturally but that had properties useful to man. People were quick to see the implications, and a rash of experiments in the synthesis of organic materials began.

Among those who were intrigued by the possibilities of this new avenue of exploration was the German August Hofmann, who was teaching school and doing chemical research in London. In 1856 he launched one of his pupils, a bright eighteen-year-old named William Perkin, on an attempt to synthesize quinine by breaking down coal tar. From what was known of the chemical formulas of both, the idea seemed reasonable. The experiment was a miserable failure, insofar as production of quinine was concerned; but at a mid-stage in Perkin's efforts, he found that he had a brilliant purple liquid which was so indelible he decided it might have possible commercial value as a dye.

He was right, and he had a gold mine. Dyes were then largely limited to the few natural plant or animal substances that the ancients had used, and this new one caused a sensation among textile manufacturers. Perkin was a rich man before he was twenty-five, and retired at thirty-five. Other chemists leaped into the field, and before long a variety of synthetic ("aniline") dyes were available.

Much of what chemists learned about the molecular structure of organic compounds during the latter half of the nineteenth century will be important to us later in this book, but for the moment it is the invention of synthetic dyes that concerns us—because they helped to illuminate the interior of the cell. It was soon learned that various substructures within the cell absorb specific dyes in varying amounts, and thus become clearer in outline under a microscope. It's the same principle as the modern medical technique of requiring a patient to drink barium before having a fluoroscopy. A stomach by itself is "transparent" to an X-ray eye, but the shape of a stomach filled with an opaque liquid like barium is clearly delineated.

In the 1880's, the German biologist Walter Flemming discovered a staining technique which revealed the presence in the cell nucleus of many tiny thread-like bodies. They came to be called chromosomes, because they absorb color. In the next series of figures (*34–37*) we have reproduced Flemming's drawings (1882) of what he observed in the cells of a salamander larva: *see page 84.*

In what has since come to be called the "resting stage," the chromosomes are jumbled up in the cell nucleus like a heap of basting threads on a sewing table (1). As cell division begins, they begin to contract, grow "plumper" (2), and start to congregate in the center of the cell (3).

Flemming's sketches do not show that the chromosomes are surrounded by a nuclear membrane in (1) and (2) and that it has ruptured in (3), thus causing the remaining stages of cell division to take place in the cytoplasm. Nor do his sketches clearly show that each chromosome is composed of two thin strands lying side by side and behaving as one unit—although he observed the fact, and described it.

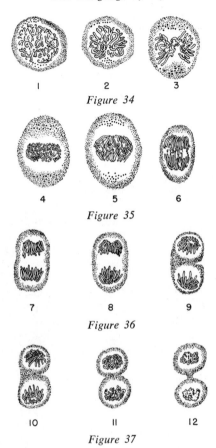

1   2   3

Figure 34

4   5   6

Figure 35

7   8   9

Figure 36

10   11   12

Figure 37

The cell elongates (4). Flemming believed that at this stage the two thin strands which together form a chromosome separate and each makes a copy of itself, thus doubling the number of chromosomes. (A few years later, Flemming's prediction was confirmed.) Then one of each of these new double-stranded bodies moves to an opposite pole of the cell [(5) and (6)]. Each takes on a V-shape, as if invisible fishermen at each pole had hooked them and were swiftly hauling them in.

When the chromosomes have divided into two groups (7), and have packed themselves into the two ends of the cell (8), nuclear membranes form around them (not shown), and the cell begins to divide (9).

The chromosomes clump more closely together (10), become increasingly less distinct as new cell walls form (11), and by the time two cells have replaced the original one, the chromosomes have again become a thread-like, jumbled mass (12). It is now known that such division and duplication of some human cells takes about an hour.

The scientific name for this process is "mitosis" (pronounced my-TOE-sis). It is the process by which the single cell that was your beginning supplied each additional cell with the same number of chromosomes, and of the same kind, as there were in the original cell—and eventually turned into *you*.

Flemming and others observed cell division in many different organisms, both plants and animals, and came to the conclusion that the process is universal. They also established beyond doubt that cells come from pre-existing cells and chromosomes from pre-existing chromosomes.

Now let us return to Weismann's germ plasm theory. He believed that germ plasm was eternal, in the sense that it was never formed anew. After it acted as the "seed" for a given part of each growing individual, it was somehow extracted and returned to the egg cells or sperm cells of that individual, and passed on by him or her to the next generation. The extraction idea was wrong, because the mosaic idea was wrong, but two ideas that grew out of Weismann's germ plasm theory were in general correct —and important to the growth of understanding about inheritance.

The first was this: If the germ plasm is never formed anew, whatever may be happening in the environment or to the individual cannot be expected to affect the germ plasm in the future. This reasoning struck at the heart of the then-widely-prevailing belief (and one that is still held by some people) that characteristics acquired during the lifetime of parents are regularly inherited by children. It was believed, for example, that a hod-carrier whose exercise has produced huge biceps will produce sons with strength and biceps equal to their father's, even without exercise; or that a child sired by a drunkard is destined to be a drunkard, too; or that children conceived late in a man's life will be smaller and weaker than previous children by the same father because the "strength" of his sperm diminishes with age. (Regarding this last belief, we now know that older parents have had greater opportunity to acquire mutations in their reproductive cells, hence may sire children with genetic defects; but if such mutation has not occurred, the sperm of a man of seventy is no different from his sperm when he was seventeen.)

To make his point, Weismann raised generation after generation of mice, cut off their tails, then asked why each new lot of mice came into the world *with* tails. Others since him have posed the same question, using such examples as the old Chinese custom of foot-binding or the traditional Jewish custom of circumcision. Why would either practice have been necessary beyond one generation if bodily changes acquired during an individual's lifetime were transmittable to his children?

The second idea that grew out of the germ plasm theory was that in *reproductive* cells of the body—that is, those that give rise to egg or sperm cells—there must be some device to prevent the passing on to offspring of all the germ plasm in the parental cells. It was known that a sperm and an egg cell blend their contents in the course of fertilization; which was another way of saying that a fertilized egg—being a combination of the two cells—would have a double dose of germ plasm. Then, in the next generation, an already doubled amount would double again. Eventually you'd have cells containing an astronomical amount of germ plasm. It just didn't make sense. Weismann said that there must be some kind of a nuclear division by which each daughter cell receives only *half* the germ plasm of the parent cell. This would allow the other half to be supplied by the fertilizing sperm cell.

And so it was, when investigators studied the division of reproductive cells. In their behavior, they *did* differ from other body cells. In 1885, the Belgian embryologist Eduard von Beneden found the "nuclear division" that Weismann had postulated. Its scientific name is "meiosis" (pronounced my-OH-sis). A good way to remember its fundamental difference from the division of other body cells is to imagine (*see Figure 38*) that the fingers on your hands

Figure 38

represent chromosomes, which in ordinary cell division engage in a game of patty-cake with someone else (the product being twice as many fingers—or chromosomes—as you began with); but in the division of sex cells, only your own two hands come together, the final product being (as we shall soon see) a reduction rather than an increase.

To review in diagrammatic form, *Figure 39* shows what happens when ordinary body cells divide.

Figure 40, however, shows in a simplified way what happens in sex-cell division. In *40C*, the dotted lines extending beyond the cell are intended to help you visualize its depth, for you must now start thinking of the cell in three dimensions. No cell is flat, and in either kind of cell division, its processes go on "in the round." But one can understand ordinary cell division without the third dimension, whereas it is crucial in sex-cell division. So please visualize the cell as having depth, with the chromosomes lying in two planes. Then, when the cell divides, there is a double split. It separates crosswise, as when you cut a biscuit in half; and each of those halves divides. The result is four cells. (*See Figure 41*.)

A. *The chromosomes (four shown here, two of each kind) congregate in the center of the cell.*
B. *Each strand makes a copy of itself and a new coupling called a centromere forms. (This is where the hook used by those imaginary fishermen a few pages back catches hold.)*
C. *Of the four A's and four B's, two of each go to one pole and two of each to the other.*
D. *And thus each new cell contains duplicates of the four chromosomes in the original cell.*

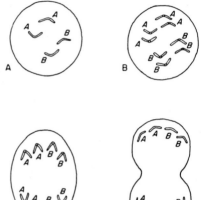

Figure 39

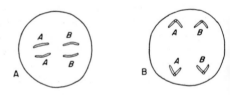

A. *The chromosomes congregate in the center of the cell, but this time in definite pairings.*
B. *They do not divide at their centromeres, but go to the poles in their original form.*
C. *And then each strand makes a duplicate of itself.*

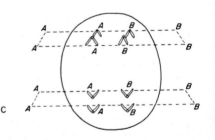

Figure 40

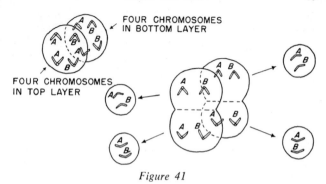

FOUR CHROMOSOMES
IN BOTTOM LAYER

FOUR CHROMOSOMES
IN TOP LAYER

Figure 41

Recapitulation: the division of body cells results in two cells where only one had been before, both cells having the same number of chromosomes as the parent cell; whereas in the division of sex cells, the initial single cell makes four, and each of the four has only half as many chromosomes as the parent. Note particularly, in addition —it's going to be important in a minute—that the two *A*'s were paired and the two *B*'s were paired when the cell began to divide and that the offspring cells now have *one or the other* member of each pair.

By the end of the nineteenth century, then, chromosomes were known to be present in most cells of an organism. It was also known that they vary in number according to the kind of organism. For instance, in the *body* cells of some flies there are eight chromosomes, two each of four kinds; in garden peas, fourteen (seven pairs); in Indian corn, twenty (ten pairs); and in mice, forty (twenty pairs). If you learned your biology a long time ago, you learned that men have forty-eight—but the number has now been revised downward to forty-six (twenty-three pairs). And in the *sex* cells of each organism, the number of chromosomes was known to be just half of what it is in other body cells—that is, one of each kind.

Cytology, the branch of science which deals with the cell and its workings, had been born; but the emphasis, understandably, was on observation and description. Although a general correlation between the nucleus and heredity had been made by the 1890's, the chromosomes had not been pinpointed as the specific agents of heredity. The possibility that there might be differences among them was not appreciated. And the full significance of their pairing had not been realized.

It would be another twenty years before the chromosomes' role was fully understood; but we're going to discuss it now, because you—unlike the biologists of the 1890's—know about Mendel's work.

Suppose, in diagramming the division of a sex cell, we make one small change in nomenclature. Instead of calling the paired chromosomes *A* and *B*, let's call one of the first pair *A* and its partner *a,* and one of the second pair *B* and its partner *b.* We now have chromosomes carrying the different alleles of two separate traits. Let's say, further, that in our first example the reproductive cell is male, and that sperm are being produced.

When the chromosomes come together and pair in the center of the cell, either *A* or *a* can be at the top, likewise for *B* and *b.* Hence (remember those coin tosses in Chapter 9), there are two possibilities as to the kinds of sperm that will be produced—and the chances of either are equal. Therefore, in any given population of newly formed

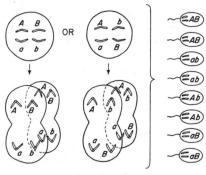

Figure 42

sperm, an equal number will have *AB, Ab, aB,* and *ab* constitutions. Expressed mathematically, the ratio is 1*AB*:1*Ab*:1*aB*:1*ab*. (*See Figure 42.*)

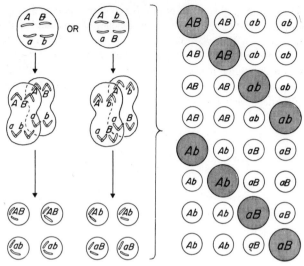

Figure 43

As *Figure 43* shows, the outcome differs a bit when egg cells are being produced. The 1:1:1:1 ratio holds true; *AB, Ab, aB,* and *ab* types will appear in approximately equal numbers in any given population; and will have an equal chance for survival. *But* in the reproduction of any given egg cell, only one—*any* one—of the four survives. The others, called "polar bodies," degenerate. The right half of *Figure 43* shows the eight combinations of eggs (large shaded circles) and polar bodies resulting from the cell divisions shown in the left half of the figure.

In the particular mating shown in *Figure 44,* the egg which survived is an *AB* type. Any one of the sperm could fertilize it, but let's say that an *AB* sperm happens to. When the cell thus acquires the proper total number of chromosomes, it can divide and duplicate in the ordinary way; and by repeated divisions it can grow into whatever organism it is destined to be.

But you can see that the new organism will not be just like the parent. The parental chromosomes were *Aa* and *Bb.* The offspring's character is *AA, BB.* And if this were the seed of a pea—forgetting for the moment that peas actually have seven pairs of chromosomes instead of the two used in the example—and you planted it, letting its blossoms pollinate themselves? You would harvest peas whose character is controlled by two dominants—smooth-surfaced yellow peas, say—which would breed "pure" in subsequent generations.

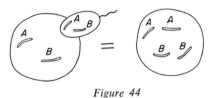

Figure 44

Chapter 12

THE MECHANISMS OF INHERITANCE

It is necessary now to turn our discussion back to the year 1859, when Charles Darwin published *Origin of Species*.

One reason that Mendel's paper, a few years later, got so little attention was that *Origin* had had such stunning impact; upon publication, and for a decade after, it was Topic A among both scientists and laymen. This occurred in part because the possibility of evolution had already been much talked about, fossil discoveries by geologists having paved the way; in part because Darwin already had a solid reputation as a naturalist; and in part because each point in his masterwork was so heavily documented that, in sum, the book was overwhelming.

Much influenced by the writings of Malthus, Darwin put forward this basic theory: each species tends to produce more individuals than the environment can support; and those who survive the resulting struggle for existence tend to do so because some trait that varies slightly from average gives them an advantage. Nature thus tends to "select" them. They live longer, have more offspring, and pass on to their progeny the small difference (a somewhat longer beak, slightly better vision, greater adaptability to temperature changes, or whatever) that gave them their initial advantage. Thus, over the course of millions of years, a succession of minute changes can bring about entirely new species.

Evolution by means of natural selection explained extinct forms of life. Fossil remains indicated the replacement of plants and animals unknown in the present by new forms slightly better adapted to the environment—but it wasn't an explanation to cheer anyone, especially the devout, in view of the prevailing belief in special creation. If God had created the plants and animals as it said in the Bible, "each according to its kind," and had thereafter found that what He had done was good, why would He allow any changes—even slight ones?

But that wasn't the worst of it. Bones of a creature not like any known ape—and, in fact, rather like a man—had been found in India in the 1830's; and the Neanderthal remains had been unearthed in Germany in 1856. Could *man,* the creature who had been made in God's image and for whose convenience the plants and animals had been designated . . . could man *also* have evolved, like them and in response to the same forces, from simpler or lower forms? The answer of society was a resounding NO. It is small wonder that this blasphemous and ego-shattering notion is still being denied both publicly and privately.[1]

Some scientists shared the emotional public reaction, or for other reasons refused to accept Darwin's view of evolution. As the years went along, however, most came to accept his "grand design," even if they disagreed with specific points. Among the dissenters were many plant and animal breeders, who had difficulty believing that species had evolved as the result of an infinite number of tiny adaptive changes over a period of many generations. There was evidence to the contrary right in their gardens or pastures. Occasionally, a "sport"—a plant or animal that differed markedly from its parents—would turn up. Furthermore, its markedly different characteristics could

---

[1] It is sometimes forgotten that the outcome of the 1925 Scopes trial in Tennessee was to find Scopes guilty and not to repeal Tennessee's law forbidding teaching about evolution. The law is still on the books.

Three other states were in the news in 1964 because of teaching practices pertaining to Darwin's theory. Out of nine new biology textbooks approved by South Carolina's education authorities for grade school or high school use in 1965, three mention evolution. No school district is required to use any of the three new texts, however, but may opt for any or all of the six others which do not mention evolution.

In Texas, there was a citizens' campaign against the use of textbooks that "teach the theory of evolution as a fact"; and, in Arizona, a clergyman led a movement to amend the State Constitution so that a teacher would be fined $100 to $500 and his credentials revoked if he lectured on the subject. Neither campaign was successful.

be passed on to the next generation (as people like Luther Burbank well knew).

By the closing years of the nineteenth century, wise biologists realized what ought to come next. Here is an excerpt from an 1899 paper by William Bateson (whom we mentioned earlier, in Chapter 1); from the attitude expressed it is easy to see why he became the great champion of Mendelism. He said:

At this time, we need no more general ideas about evolution. We need particular knowledge of the evolution of particular forms. What we first require is to know what happens when a variety is crossed with its nearest allies. If the result is to have a scientific value, it is almost absolutely necessary that the off-spring of such crossing should then be examined statistically. It must be recorded how many of the offspring resembled each parent, and how many showed characters intermediate between those of the parents. If the parents differ in several characters, the offspring must be examined . . . in respect to each of those characters separately.[2]

Among botanists or zoologists who were engaged at that time in studies of hybridization were the Dutch Hugo de Vries, the German Karl Correns, and the Austrian Erich Tschermak. Like Bateson, they recognized the need to "examine the offspring statistically," and were in the process of doing so. In 1900, the story goes, each of the three was ready to publish what he thought to be original work showing that there are constant numerical ratios in inheritance; each of the three independently found Mendel's paper and realized that the discovery had already been made; and each then published his findings as confirmation of Mendel's theory.

Scientists are as gossipy as any other group of humans; and old-timers still speculate as to whether the three-way but independent "discovery" of Mendel really happened that way. Some suggest that De Vries and Correns had both found the long-buried monograph on peas before 1900; that De Vries might have yielded to the temptation

---

[2] Quoted by H. F. Roberts in his *Plant Hybridization before Mendel* (Princeton: Princeton University Press, 1929).

to appropriate Mendel's conclusions as his own; and had written a paper in which he neglected to give credit where credit was due. Correns, the story continues, saw a second of his contemporary's papers while it was still in proof—and let him know that *he* had read Mendel's monograph too, thus allowing De Vries to make suitable changes before his second paper went to press. Meanwhile, Tschermak had also discovered Mendel's work, which he cited in a paper he had written but not published. Upon getting a reprint of De Vries' first paper, he realized the importance of his find and hurried publication.

This story is difficult to prove or disprove. Perhaps it libels De Vries, for he may have gotten his ideas by reading Mendel's paper and then quite honestly may have forgotten where they came from. This is not uncommon in science. But evidence in old journals and correspondence[3] makes one also concede the possibility that what has been described as one of the most famous coincidences of science was not all that coincidental. Then as now, scientists were prone to "talk shop" and traveled about giving lectures or attending meetings, so it is reasonable to believe that some hint of what any one of the men had found would have reached the ears of the others.

Whatever the details of timing and motivation may have been, the publication of three papers within a few months of each other, all by well-known scientists, all crediting Mendel for his work and all confirming it, commanded widespread attention in the scientific world. Thus, sixteen years after his death, the Abbot of Brünn got the hearing he had been denied in life. What he had to say now made sense, too, for his laws provided an explanation for variation, which Darwin could not account for.

Before the rediscovery of Mendel's work, inheritance was widely believed to be the result of "blending," a process that caused offspring to be intermediate between the two parents. Fleeming Jenkin, a Scottish engineer, had pointed out in 1867 that if this were so, the new variations assumed by Darwin to account for evolution would be

3 Ibid.

quickly "swamped out" through crossing with old forms. (Take four ounces of colored water and four ounces of clear water and mix them. Then take four ounces of this mixture and add to it another four ounces of clear water . . . and so on, following the same procedure, until you have ten times "crossed" the original colored water with clear water. By the tenth mixing, inasmuch as only 1/1024th part of the eight ounces of water will be colored, it will seem to have completely disappeared.)

This objection was regarded by Darwin as so serious that in his later life he resorted to the hypothesis of the inheritance of acquired characteristics to explain the phenomenon of variation. Mendel, of course, showed that inheritance is not blending; that unlike alleles emerge from a hybrid exactly as they entered it. (The colored water may not be visible, but it's still there.) While we now know that there are exceptions to Mendel's generalization about the non-contamination of individual alleles, it still remains a satisfactory answer to Jenkin's apparently lethal objection to Darwin's theory.

Did Mendel realize the full significance of his findings in relation to this blending inheritance objection to Darwin's hypothesis? We know that Mendel read *Origin of Species,* for there exists a copy from his monastery in which marginal notes appear in his handwriting. It is difficult to believe he did not see this important point. If so, why did he not refer to the *Origin?* Perhaps because he read it *after* he published his findings. Perhaps because he believed that Darwin's concept ran counter to the views of the Church.

Sir Gavin de Beer, former director of the British Museum of Natural History, has written,[4] "At the time when Mendel wrote, only a dozen years or so had elapsed since the epidemic of revolutions in Europe in 1848, and the Austrian emperor had concluded a concordat with the Vatican which imposed strict censorship not only on newspapers and expressions of public opinion, but also on

[4] In "Mendel, Darwin, and the Centre of Science," *The Listener,* March 11, 1965.

university teaching. If Mendel had mentioned Darwin's name, it would have been more than Mendel's job as an Augustinian canon was worth."

We shall never know the full story, for we can never go back and read Mendel's mind.

The rediscovery of Mendel's work was timed well, because by 1900 biologists were no longer obsessively interested in tracing the evolutionary history and relationships of various organisms (as had been the case during the years following publication of *Origin of Species*). They were increasingly concerned about the creation of *new* species, and therefore they found this provocative idea of Mendel's an exciting one to test on something other than peas. They grew and hybridized evening primroses, wheat, sheep, pigeons, beans, butterflies, snapdragons, mice, rabbits, corn, and chickens—and filled the professional journals with results that on the whole confirmed Mendel but sometimes appeared contradictory.

The first decade of twentieth-century biology is a perfect example of how science characteristically advances. In seeking explanations for experimental results which sometimes agreed with Mendel's findings but not always, investigators of that day often came up with theories that were half-right and half-wrong. They sometimes had brilliant flashes of intuition, sometimes clung irrationally to traditional but newly indefensible positions, often were most cogent when the premises on which they based their reasoning were false. They followed various leads down all manner of pathways, including a number of blind alleys. But little by little, as if groping in a dark room lit by occasional flashes of light, they found and fitted together the jigsaw puzzle that Mendel had presented to them.

Here are some of the steps in the process:

In 1902, the German embryologist Theodor Boveri (using the eggs of the sea urchin) had provided the first experimental proof that specific chromosomes differ in their effects on development, and that development is normal only when an organism has a complete set of chromosomes. By 1905, several investigators—the American cytologists W. S. Sutton and C. E. McClung among them—

had discovered the presence in cells of some animals of what they called an "accessory" chromosome—an unpaired one; and had observed a few peculiarities in the behavior of others. So they were sure that the chromosomes are *not* all alike. This belief, plus the by-then-well-known processes of chromosome behavior during cell division, meant only one thing to scientists like Sutton. In one of his papers, he said, "I . . . call attention to the probability that the association of paternal and maternal chromosomes in pairs and their subsequent separation during the reducing division . . . may constitute the physical basis of the Mendelian law of heredity."

There were dissenters, Bateson among them; but even among those who granted that chromosomes might be the carriers of heredity, there was disagreement as to how they did it. Inasmuch as peas have only seven pairs of chromosomes but possess far more than the seven traits that Mendel studied, it was obvious that the chromosomes couldn't be Mendel's "elements." Hence the idea took hold early that the units of heredity—which by 1905 or so were generally being called "factors"—must be carried *in* or *by* the chromosomes. Weismann postulated that each chromosome carried a full assortment of *all* the units of heredity (he called them "ids") that go to make up the mature organism. Correns and a great many others liked the "spireme" theory, which held that the chromosomes weren't really separate when first spotted as a tangled mass in the cell; instead, they began as one long thread which broke apart into segments upon cell division.

A real sticker was Mendel's insistence that factors were transmitted from parent to progeny without change or contamination. Plants and animals kept popping up with characters that were intermediate between known factors —three shades of red and three shades of purple, for example, from parents whose flowers showed only one value of each color. The "blending" idea was out; but maybe—this was Bateson's idea—maybe some factors "fractionate" in the course of separation and recombine during fertilization. Or maybe, he and others argued, Mendel's hypothesis of "antagonistic factors" (dominance and recessiveness) wasn't quite right; maybe what happened in the recessive form was that some necessary ingredient got left out, as when a cook forgets baking powder and the biscuits don't rise. Thus was born the "presence and absence" theory, a most ingenious one. It went this way:

If *Aa* stands for coat color in mice (*A* being black; *a,* white), a white mouse (*aa*) will be white not because two factors for whiteness are present but because a factor for blackness (*A*) is absent. Thus a white mouse is really a deprived black mouse. This was a persuasive explanation when the trait one was using as an example was recessive. But what about hornlessness in cattle? When you crossed polled (hornless) cattle with a breed having horns, hornlessness was dominant. Surely two *absent* factors couldn't have an effect? The "presence and absence" theory lost its appeal when its proponents had to explain the dominance of hornlessness by saying that the factor *for* horns was really present, but that another factor (X?) was present, too—its function being to inhibit the activity of the factor for horns.

Such elaborations finally provoked a protest from a tall bearded zoologist from Columbia University. At the annual meeting of the American Breeders' Association in 1909, Thomas Hunt Morgan began his remarks by saying,

> In the modern interpretation of Mendelism, facts are being transformed into factors at a rapid rate. If one factor will not explain the facts, then two are invoked; if two prove insufficient, three will sometimes work out. The superior jugglery sometimes necessary to account for the results may blind us, if taken too naïvely, to the common-place that the results are often so excellently "explained" because the explanation was invented to explain them. We work backwards from the facts to the factors, and then, presto! explain the facts by the very factors that we invented to account for them.

The next speaker was R. A. Emerson, scheduled to read a paper on coat-color inheritance in mottled beans. He reported that a previously postulated one-factor explanation of their behavior did not square with the results of his work with the same plant material, but that the results were readily accounted for if one assumed *two* pairs of segregating factors. The audience howled. "If one factor does not explain the facts, then two are invoked": Morgan had won *that* round, all right. (But Emerson eventually had the last word on the matter of mottled beans. Some years later, it was clearly established that their coat-color *is* indeed controlled by two pairs of factors.)

Among the famous experiments of the early twentieth century was one, in 1906, by Bateson and the English botanist R. C. Punnett, with two varieties of sweet peas. One had purple flowers and a long pollen grain, the other had red flowers and a round pollen grain; and if these four traits segregated independently (as Mendel had reported for garden peas), the second hybrid generation should have yielded four distinct types in a ratio of 9:3: 3:1. Out of 256 plants, for instance, this is what *should* have happened:

Purple-long	*Purple-round*	*Red-long*	*Red-round*
144	48	48	16

but this is what *did* happen:

177	15	15	49

If you'll add up the ratio of purples to reds, and the ratio of longs to rounds, you'll see that in each case it's 3:1. But the four traits certainly hadn't segregated independently. In fact, purple had tended to stay with long, and red had stayed with round.

This, and other experiments that showed similar "coupling," caused Punnett to say (in 1911), ". . . Nor for the present can we suggest why certain factors should be linked together in the peculiar way that we have reason to suppose they are. . . . Nevertheless the phenomena are very definite, and it is not unlikely that a further study of them may throw important light on the architecture of the living cell."[5]

Morgan, despite his scorn of efforts to transform facts into factors, was intrigued by problems of inheritance. He

---

[5] From *Mendelism,* by R. C. Punnett (New York: The Macmillan Company, 1911).

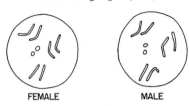

FEMALE   MALE

Figure 45

had done much research on processes of cell growth in
frogs, and kept informed as to advances in cytology . . .
such as discoveries from 1905 onward that the sex of an
organism makes a difference in chromosomal number or
arrangement. In some animals, the male lacks one of a
pair of chromosomes, or one chromosome of a pair is
differently shaped. In other animals, it is the female in
whose cells there is deviation from the normal complement of paired sets. This was, as you have guessed, the
"accessory" chromosome mentioned earlier.

As an example, *Figure 45* shows the cell of a fly. The
four pairs of chromosomes in the female are alike; but
the chromosome sketched at bottom right in the male cell
has a "hook." The chromosome at the left of each bottom
pair was named the X chromosome. The hooked one was
called the Y chromosome, and since it is found only in
the males of its species, the assumption upon its discovery
was that it had something to do with sex determination.

Indeed it did have, as subsequent research showed. One
of the great achievements of the time was to discover the
mechanism that creates an approximately equal number
of both sexes in all living things, a problem that had long
been a puzzler. Here's why:

When a reproductive cell (one that makes egg cells in
the female or sperm cells in the male) divides, one-half of
each pair of chromosomes goes into the new cell. Thus,

FEMALE   MALE

Figure 46

in the four cells produced by a female, all four will be just like the parent cell: each will contain an X chromosome. In the division of a male cell, however, two of the four progeny will have an X chromosome and the other two will have a Y chromosome. (*See Figure 46.*)

Then, if an egg cell (all of which have X chromosomes) is fertilized by an X-bearing sperm, a female results. But if a Y-bearing sperm fertilizes that X-bearing cell, a male results. (*See Figure 47.*)

Thus, however you combine the four cells that result from the division of any particular two, equal numbers of the sexes will result. (*See Figure 48.*)

And here's a reprise of a previous comment. Bear in mind that chance alone determines which kind of sex chromosome is introduced by a sperm into any given egg cell. Sperm in the mass are approximately 50 per cent X-carrying and approximately 50 per cent Y-carrying, but—just as each tossed coin has an equal chance of

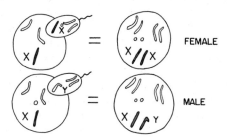

Figure 47

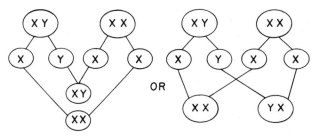

Figure 48

coming up heads or tails—each sperm has an equal chance of carrying an X or a Y chromosome. The egg is therefore equally likely to be fertilized by either kind.

In human reproduction, millions of sperm are discharged by the male during mating, and move up the Fallopian tubes in the female. The sperm which gets there first is presumably the one that fertilizes the egg and thus determines the sex of the child that will develop from that fertilized egg. If the sperm carries an X chromosome, the child is a daughter; if a Y chromosome, the child is a son. In short, the father who faces a dinner table full of female faces has only himself and the laws of chance to blame.

So much for the mechanics of sex determination. Did the X and Y chromosomes also have something to do with the inheritance of characteristics which appear only in one sex? There was, for example, the fact that in humans the inherited diseases of hemophilia[6] and color blindness are much more frequent in males than in females. In cats, the "calico" coat color is restricted to females—or if it appears in a male, he's sterile. Poultry breeders knew that in crossing a Brown Leghorn with a heavily pigmented breed called Silky, the offspring turned out differently depending on whether you used a Silky hen or a Silky cock in the parentage. Why? If sex chromosomes *did* carry factors governing inheritance . . .

Morgan was a man who thought big. He decided that an answer to some of these riddles lay in the observation of massive numbers of some living organism. He chose a

---

[6] Anyone who wants to play the game of "if only . . ." can do so with the most famous case of hemophilia in history. Queen Victoria of England passed on the gene for the "bleeder's disease" (in which the blood does not clot normally) to her daughter Alice, who in turn passed it on to *her* daughter, the wife of Czar Nicholas II of Russia. In consequence, their son the Czarevitch Alexei was a hemophiliac. Doctors could do nothing for him, but the monk Rasputin said he could cure the boy. Thus the Czar and Czarina came under the influence of Rasputin; and from him spread the corruption and political decay that resulted in the Bolshevik Revolution and laid the groundwork for the present regime in the U.S.S.R.

tiny fruit fly, *Drosophila melanogaster* (pronounced Dro-SOPH-i-la MEL-an-o-GAS-ter), the kind that buzzes around ripe bananas.[7] This little creature is an ideal research material because it grows to maturity in ten days, requires nothing more fancy than yeast for food, can live by the hundreds in half-pint glass bottles, and has only four pairs of chromosomes. This latter characteristic makes it if not actually easy to study at least easier to study than an organism with five times as many chromosomes.

With this choice, a new period in biological research was inaugurated. From Morgan's time onward, the great discoveries in genetics have resulted from studies of smaller and smaller organisms, primarily because they can be grown in huge numbers at low cost and many generations can be studied within a relatively short time. But it has not been easy to make the non-scientist realize that the organism in question is only a tool.

The young son of one of Morgan's colleagues was in the third grade when his teacher began a what-does-your Daddy-do-for-a-living poll. The child replied, "My Daddy counts flies for Columbia University." A good straight answer—one that children of some geneticists would still give to a similar question, and that would still cause their elders to snicker. The average layman tends to equate research *on* fruit flies with a burning interest *in* fruit flies, an interest that is pretty low on his list of what a red-blooded American man ought to spend his time thinking about.

The gap in his understanding is his failure to realize that whatever scientists learn about fruit flies, they have learned about *him*. Living organisms are fundamentally alike, even if one kind buzzes around a banana and another kind

---

[7] To an entomologist, true fruit flies belong to the family *Trapaneidae*. Drosophila should properly be called a vinegar fly. To call it a fruit fly sometimes causes it to be confused with the Mediterranean fruit fly (*Ceratitis capitata*), a pest which the United States Department of Agriculture is making heroic efforts to exclude from this country. However, we have decided to call harmless Drosophila a fruit fly because, over the years, this terminology has become so common among biologists.

peels it. Although the sketches of chromosome arrangement in this chapter are representations of cell nuclei in Drosophila, they are correct in principle for your cells, too. All you have to do is to visualize twenty-three pairs of chromosomes behaving like the four pairs sketched.

One of Morgan's most important experiments (not because of its intrinsic brilliance but because it turned him from a doubting Thomas into an enthusiastic geneticist and eventually into a giant in the field) resulted from the discovery of a white-eyed fly among a batch of normal red-eyed ones. This trait was obviously the result of a spontaneous mutation, since there were no others like it, and Morgan recognized its potential usefulness as a genetic marker. So he bred it—a male—to a normal red-eyed female.

All the offspring had red eyes. So far, so good: it was as Mendel had said. The red-eye factor must be dominant, the white-eye factor recessive. The offspring of the second generation were close enough to the Mendelian 3:1 ratio, too: 3470 red eyes to 782 white eyes. But there was something very odd about the whites. They were all males. And since the total number of flies in the experiment was 4252, the finding of 782 white-eyed flies not one of which was female ruled out coincidence. There *had* to be a connection between the factor for white eyes and the sex of the individual; and since sex was determined by the chromosomes, the chromosomes must carry the factors of inheritance. Morgan was convinced. He had seen for himself.

By 1915, he and his colleagues had studied the inheritance of more than 100 traits in fruit flies, and had discovered that some 20 of them were linked to the sex of the fly. They had learned that the Y chromosome is associated with maleness, but that its presence doesn't have a positive effect on such notably sex-linked traits as eye color. However, its partner X chromosome *does*. And that's why all those white-eyed flies were males. The reason is as follows:

The cross that Morgan made, remember, was of a red-eyed female and a white-eyed male. Assume that all her egg cells contain X chromosomes carrying a factor for red eyes (*A*), whereas the male's X chromosomes carry a factor for white eyes (*a*). However, only half his sperm cells contain X chromosomes; the other half contain Y chromosomes, which are empty insofar as an allele for eye color is concerned.

Therefore, any egg fertilized by an X-carrying sperm would grow into a red-eyed female—red-eyed because *A* is dominant to *a,* and female because the fertilized egg contains two X chromosomes. And any egg fertilized by a Y-carrying sperm would grow into a red-eyed male—red-eyed because the *A* in the egg cell is the *only* factor for

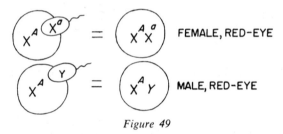

Figure 49

eye color, and male because the fertilized egg contains XY chromosomes. Thus, in the first hybrid generation, all the offspring—whether male or female—would be red-eyed. That was what Morgan had found in his experiment.

Each of those hybrids would produce two kinds of sex cells which, if crossed, would yield offspring as diagrammed below. (*See page 108*.) And this was also what Morgan had found: a Mendelian 3:1 ratio, but with a sex-linkage of white eyes to maleness.

This is the genetic explanation also of hemophilia and color blindness in humans. We may as well begin to use modern terminology, "genes" having replaced "factors" during Morgan's lifetime; so, read *A* above as the gene that enables an individual to differentiate between red and green, *a* as its defective form; or *A* as the gene that controls normal blood-clotting, *a* as its defective form—and you'll see why mothers carry the defect but sons show it.

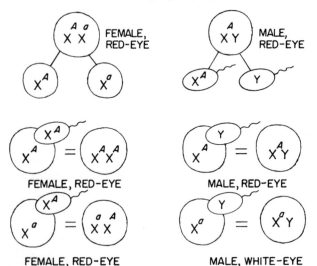

Figure 50

If a woman has inherited one normal and one defective gene—say, for color blindness—the normal gene will be dominant and she will have normal color vision. However, half her egg cells (on the average) will carry the defective gene, the other half will carry the normal one—and it is a matter of chance as to which kind is fertilized. Since her husband's Y chromosome, the one that creates a son rather than a daughter, carries no gene for red-green color discrimination, the single gene the wife contributes will determine whether a male child will be normal or defective with regard to this sex-linked trait. Therefore, half her sons (on the average, again) will be color blind.

It is appropriate here to say something about Morgan's research methods.

No one has ever seen a gene (except indirectly through an electron microscope, and then only recently). Genes are so small that if you could string all that are present in all the cells of your body into one long filament and then wind it back and forth (like this: ☰) on the head of a common pin, you would cover only one-half of 1 per cent of the pin's surface. Therefore Morgan, and every geneticist who followed him, was forced to "see" the genes by observing their effect on a whole organism.

For example, if one notices in a few cases that certain traits "follow" the X chromosome and postulates therefore that genes for those traits must be *in* the X chromosome, one checks the hypothesis by making every imaginable variety of cross between individuals exhibiting sex-linked traits and those who do not. You can consider your hypothesis proved if, in cross after cross after cross, the particular traits you are watching continue to follow the X chromosome.[8]

Likewise, if you notice that certain traits are not only sex-linked in the broad sense of being carried by the X chromosome but are also inherited together (like purple flower and long pollen in sweet peas), you test both the fact of linkage and identify *which* traits are linked by raising additional huge batches of flies and record the frequency with which the traits you think are linked actually do stay together in succeeding generations.

The way you do it, incidentally, is by hand; and it's drudgery. You place under a microscope each of the hundreds of offspring of fruit flies—which are small enough to start with, but must then be studied for tiny variations in bristles, wings, faceting and color of the eye, and so forth. Among the difficulties is the one of labeling what you see—a problem comparable to that of a city planner finding names for streets in a new sub-

8 Testcross methods—the check-and-double-check techniques used to make sure that sex-linked traits *do* follow the X chromosome —have an elegance about them that is exciting to professionals or to students already sophisticated in the ways of science. We judged them to be too complicated for the general reader, but if you're interested we recommend Morgan's *Mechanism of Mendelian Heredity* (New York: Henry Holt & Company, 1915) or Sturtevant and Beadle's *Introduction to Genetics* (Philadelphia: W. B. Saunders Company, 1939; New York, Dover Publications paperback, 1962).

division. For example, in Morgan's and other labs, the differences in length, density, or shape of just the *bristles* in flies of differing inheritance resulted in such descriptive labels as scute, singed, forked, bobbed, stubble, spineless, hairless, and shaven. And to show how much variation there is in both the eye color of flies *and* in the English language, here are some of the labels used to identify the traits for eyes in varying shades of red: ruby, vermilion, garnet, carnation, cinnabar, scarlet, pink, cardinal, claret.

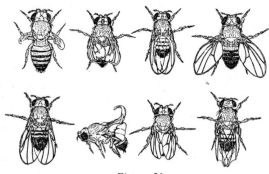

Figure 51

Named for variations in wings or bristles, the flies sketched above are, left to right: Vestigial (wing), Rudimentary (wing), Forked (bristle), Dichaete (wing), Stubble (bristle), Curled (wing), Miniature (wing), and Scute Crossveinless Cut (which means absence of bristles, without crossveins in the wings, and with blunt-edged wings that look cut). These sketches were made many years ago by Miss Edith M. Wallace for Thomas Hunt Morgan; she did them by observation under a microscope.

Someone once said that God must have created Drosophila especially for Thomas Hunt Morgan. In any case, in the course of his years at Columbia and then at Caltech, he turned it into one of the most famous experimental organisms in the world. His "Drosophila school" of genetic research resulted in the growing and counting of millions of fruit flies in laboratories in every nation. And out of painstaking work on such a grand scale came a big discovery: inherited traits in Drosophila fall into one of four linkage groups.

There are more than 100 known traits carried in the X chromosome. Two other groups, each of 100 or more traits, tend to appear together. And one linkage group includes only half a dozen or so traits. (All figures have been updated to the present—the known totals were less in Morgan's time, although the proportions were the same.)

Now, how many pairs of chromosomes are there in Drosophila? Four. And how big are they? Three pairs are relatively large and one pair is very much smaller. It therefore made good sense to postulate that there would be fewer genes in the little pair than in each of the larger pairs. In short, three large linkage groups and one small one squared very nicely with the relative size of chromosomes as seen in the cell (*Figure 52*).

Things were knitting together. With the discovery that there are five linkage groups in a kind of fly known to have five pairs of chromosomes, and ten linkage groups in field corn, which has ten pairs of chromosomes, there virtually ceased to be any argument among scientists as to the site of inheritance.

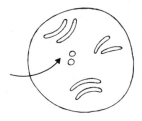

Figure 52

Chapter 13

GENETIC CHANGES,
NATURAL AND MAN-MADE

The discovery of linkage groups was a great step forward. But a major mystery remained. Why is it that linked traits don't *always* stay together?

In Bateson and Punnett's sweet pea experiment, remember, most of the progeny had the purple flower-long pollen or red flower-round pollen combination of the parents; but a few turned up which exhibited one of the linked traits or the other, not both. Morgan had had the same result in crossing a normal gray-bodied long-winged fly with a black-bodied fly whose wings were so small and deformed that he labeled the type "vestigial." The black body and vestigial wings were inherited together most of the time, but in about 8 per cent of second-generation crosses, the black body trait and the vestigial wing trait separated and recombined differently in the offspring—resulting in black-bodied, long-winged flies or gray-bodied vestigials. And this kind of recombination was by no means uncommon. What caused it?

After doing hundreds of breeding experiments, Morgan and others found that although the percentages of recombination varied greatly—from almost 50 per cent to less than 1 per cent—the figures were remarkably constant when particular traits were being studied. For example, whenever anyone crossed a yellow-bodied white-eyed female with a gray-bodied red-eyed male, the second generation recombination rate was close to 1.5 per cent. If the mating was between a vestigial-winged cinnabar-eyed female and a long-winged red-eyed male, the recombination rate was approximately 10 per cent. Likewise with a miniature-winged white-eyed female and a long-winged red-eyed male: recombinations occurred at a rate of about 33 per cent.

What was the reason for this incomplete linkage?

Suppose, said Morgan, (as illustrated in *Figures 53–55*) that within a given chromosome the genes were arranged in linear order and that in the early stages of cell division, when the chromosomes were in their tangled, twisted, thread-like stage, one chromosome should happen to lie across another one and that a break were to occur at the point of overlap; after which, in the course of mending the break, the chromosomes exchanged their parts. Morgan called this process "crossing-over."

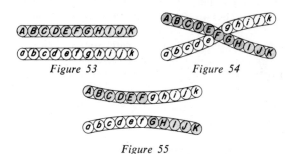

Figure 53   *Figure 54*

Figure 55

And what would happen in terms of inheritance?

As *Figure 56* shows, if *no* crossing-over occurred during the division of a reproductive cell—in other words, if each egg or sperm cell got one of the other of the original parental chromosomes—half the new cells would contain chromosome 1 and half would contain chromosome 2 and therefore traits governed by genes *A-K* or *a-k* would appear in subsequent offspring, as firmly linked as in the parent.

But, as *Figure 57* shows, if crossing-over *had* occurred, half of the sperm or egg cells would contain a chromosome we have labeled 1/2; and half would contain chromo-

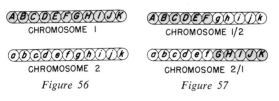

CHROMOSOME 1   CHROMOSOME 1/2

CHROMOSOME 2   CHROMOSOME 2/1

Figure 56   *Figure 57*

some 2/1 and thus individuals would appear in which traits *A-F* were now linked with *g-k,* and *a-f* with *G-K.*

If *Ff* controlled purpleness or redness in sweet peas and *Gg* controlled long or round pollen grains, crossing-over would explain the results in Bateson and Punnett's sweet-pea experiment. Most of the parental cells, in dividing to form egg or pollen cells, had sent on whole chromosomes to the next generation, with the result that *FG* and *fg* remained together and expressed themselves in the off-spring as purple-long (*FG*) or red-round (*fg*). But in some of the parental cells, crossing-over had occurred, and in the chromosomes of *their* offspring *F* now lay beside *g* and *f* next to *G*. This would explain why a few of the progeny were purple flowered with round pollen (*Fg*) or red flowered with long pollen (*fG*).

Morgan also postulated double crossovers (*Figure 58*) which, when the parts had exchanged, could be labeled 1/2/1 or 2/1/2.

CHROMOSOME 1

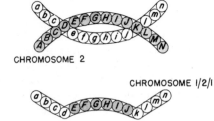

CHROMOSOME 2

CHROMOSOME 1/2/1

CHROMOSOME 2/1/2

Figure 58

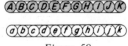

Figure 59

Furthermore, he said, the amount of crossing-over be-tween chromosomes logically depends on the linear dis-tance between specific genes. For example, in the pair shown in *Figure 59*, there is a much greater chance that the chromosomes will tangle somewhere between *Bb* and *Jj* than between *Bb* and *Cc*. Therefore, wouldn't the constant "crossover percentages"—such as the 1.5 per cent characteristic of the yellow body-white eye trait, the 10 per cent characteristic of vestigial wing-cinnabar eye, and the 33 per cent characteristic of miniature wing-white eye—indicate the linear distance between the genes that control those traits?

Wouldn't the genes for yellow body and white eye be closer together within the chromosome than the genes for miniature wing and white eye? (Within the X chromosome, that is, since these are sex-linked traits.) As for vestigial wing and cinnabar, wouldn't they—with a 10 per cent crossover rate—be farther apart than vestigial wing and black body, which recombine approximately 8 per cent of the time? (Within the second chromosome, presumably, since these traits are in the second linkage group.)

It was A. H. Sturtevant, one of Morgan's students and later a colleague, who had originally postulated that genes must be arranged in a linear series. In 1913 he set out to test his hypothesis by "mapping" the chromosomes in fruit flies. As his standard unit of measure, he arbitrarily took the distance that will give (on the average) one crossover per hundred fertilized eggs. Thus, the genes for vestigial and cinnabar, with 10 per cent of crossing-over, are 10 units apart. And since vestigial and black body, with 8 per cent crossing-over, are 8 units apart, a map of the second chromosome could begin to take shape. *Figure 60A* shows the beginning of such a map; *60B* is a comparable beginning for the X chromosome.

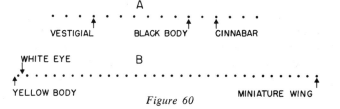

Figure 60

As such maps—assigning fixed spots in each chromosome to each gene—were put together, geneticists could begin to predict the amount of crossing-over that ought to occur and what traits the offspring of any cross ought to exhibit; test the prediction by making the cross; and call it confirmed if the offspring turned up with the predicted traits in the predicted proportion.

Arguments over the lab coffee cups or in professional journals were fearsome when "stubble" and "spineless" or "forked" and "bar" turned up at identical points on a chromosome. Sometimes new experiments resolved the dispute and located the two genes in question a half-unit in one direction or the other, but sometimes new experiments merely confirmed that two—or more—genes apparently occupied the same position in chromosomes of the same kind. Thus geneticists discovered that there can be multiple alleles of any given trait.

Take the 1.5 position in the X chromosome, for example. In that position, some flies carry a gene which acts to form red eyes, others have a gene for cherry eyes, still others have a gene for apricot eyes. There are many other variants; and the presumption is that since red eyes are dominant to all the others, the variants are all different mutant alleles of the gene for red.

A human example of multiple allelism occurs in blood groups. There are three genes in man which control the formation of distinctive kinds of blood corpuscles—A, B, and O—each of which presumably occupies the same position in its chromosome. A and B possess no dominance relative to each other, hence an AB blood type occurs; but A and B are each dominant to O—and this is the basis of using blood tests in paternity cases.

Two parents with O-type blood can have only O-type children. A person with AB blood can have no O-type children, and neither of his parents can have been O-type. The only way that persons with A or B type blood can conceive an O-type child is if both have AO or BO genes and the two recessive O's come together in the child.

Parents*			Children possible	Children not possible
A (AA or AO)	**A** (AA or AO)		**A** or **O**	**AB** or **B**
A (AA or AO)	**B** (BB or BO)		**A, B, AB,** or **O**	
A (AA or AO)	**AB** (AB)		**A, B,** or **AB**	**O**
A (AA or AO)	**O** (OO)		**A** or **O**	**AB** or **B**
B (BB or BO)	**B** (BB or BO)		**B** or **O**	**A** or **AB**
B (BB or BO)	**AB** (AB)		**A, B,** or **AB**	**O**
B (BB or BO)	**O** (OO)		**B** or **O**	**A** or **AB**
AB (AB)	**AB** (AB)		**A, B,** or **AB**	**O**
AB (AB)	**O** (OO)		**A** or **B**	**O** or **AB**
O (OO)	**O** (OO)		**O**	**A, B,** or **AB**

* Boldface letters are blood type; lightface letters in parentheses are genetic constitution.

Blood tests can't prove, of course, that so-and-so was the father of a given child; but they can provide convincing evidence that he *wasn't*. In the famous Charlie Chaplin paternity case of the 1940's, the baby's blood was B, the mother's A, and the actor's O—which would seem to indicate that Chaplin couldn't have been the baby's father. It is ironic that he was adjudged to have been so, anyway. (Blood group data are not admitted as evidence by some states in cases of disputed parentage.)

Despite the fact that man has 46 chromosomes, the locations of genes within them could probably be mapped. The difficulty is that one can't breed man by the tens of millions, keep him and his progeny in half-pint glass bottles, and tick off a new generation every ten days. But maps of chromosomes in fruit flies and in field corn were constructed during the first third of the century; and they did indeed seem to prove that genes have fixed positions in a linear series—like beads on a necklace of life—and that crossing-over is a normal phenomenon of inheritance.

However, crossing-over causes reassortment without fundamental change of partners. Individual alleles are still paired. Surely some much more drastic kind of rearrangement must be responsible for gross changes in organisms—changes of such severe or dramatic nature that never-before-seen traits arise, or a certain percentage of off-spring die, or the fertility of those who live is affected?

Let's take, for example, what *usually* happens when a white-eyed Drosophila female mates with a red-eyed male (*Figure 61*). All the eggs she produces are of one kind: they carry a gene for white eyes on the X chromosome. His sperm, however, are of two kinds: those that include an X chromosome and its gene for red eyes, and those that contain the "passive" Y chromosome. In such a mating, all the daughters normally have red eyes and all the sons have white eyes.

But occasionally—say, once in a thousand or two thousand times—exceptions occur: daughters with white eyes and sons with red eyes appear. These latter, however, produce sperm that lacks motility. There was also a puzzling problem in connection with certain females, who appeared to have normally pigmented red eyes, but who always died before maturity.

Calvin Bridges, first a student of Morgan and then a colleague, had a theory as to what happens in cases like these. He called the process "non-disjunction." It might

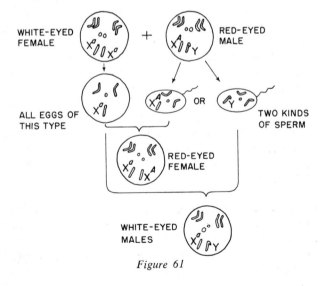

Figure 61

be, he said, that the X chromosomes sometimes don't assort naturally. *Both* X chromosomes might go into the mature egg cell, or with equal frequency they might go into the polar bodies, leaving the mature egg cell with no X chromosome at all. Such an occurrence is diagrammed in *Figure 62*.

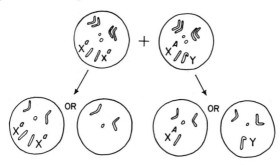

Figure 62

Four kinds of offspring would be possible (*Figure 63*).

Bridges knew that maleness or femaleness in Drosophila (unlike man) correlates with the possession of, respectively, one or two X chromosomes. In theory, therefore, the aberrant white-eyed females found in the laboratory should have two X chromosomes inherited from their mother and a passive Y chromosome inherited from their father, as in *Figure 63A*. He got out a microscope and examined the cells of such flies; and they did indeed have the abnormal chromosome distribution that he had postulated!

Bridges also examined the cells of red-eyed males who were, in effect, sterile. *Their* chromosomal makeup also matched the theoretical possibility diagrammed in *Figure 63B*. The presence of the single X chromosome with its gene for red eyes would account for their sex and eye color, but the absence of a Y chromosome clearly had some effect on the motility of the sperm they produced.

And what about the red-eyed females that failed to mature? Bridges later dubbed them "superfemales" because their cells contained the triplet X chromosomes

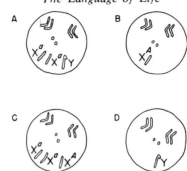

A. *A union of the egg cell carrying both X chromosomes (with their gene for white eyes) and a sperm with a Y chromosome.*

B. *An egg cell lacking an X chromosome which had been fertilized by a sperm cell carrying an X chromosome with a gene for red eyes.*

C. *An egg cell that had inherited both X chromosomes (with genes for white eyes) and that had been fertilized by an X-carrying sperm (with its gene for red eyes).*

D. *An egg cell which had acquired no X chromosome and had been fertilized by a sperm containing a Y chromosome.*

Figure 63

shown in *Figure 63C*. The dominant gene for red eyes obviously blankets the two recessive genes for white eyes. Because X chromosomes determine many more traits than eye color, it seemed likely that flies burdened with a complete extra set of directions would be badly flawed —just as a cake is, when its maker inadvertently doubles the amount of one ingredient. It was not surprising, then, that the superfemales died young.

Bridges didn't find the type of fly whose existence he had postulated and that we have diagrammed in *Figure 63D*. The assumption is that the complete lack of an X chromosome so impairs it that it dies in the egg stage.

By bringing together the genetic theory and the cytological facts, Bridges cinched the case for genes in chromosomes as the mechanism of heredity. His work, published in 1916, convinced all but the most refractory of skeptics.

Paradoxically, William Bateson—the militant defender of Mendelism—was one of these. He remained a skeptic to the end of his life.

Incidentally, Mongolian idiocy is an example of non-disjunction in humans. The unfortunate infant develops from a fertilized egg to which one parent contributed the usual complement of 23 chromosomes but one parent contributed 24—the twenty-fourth being a duplicate of a particular one of the others. The extra dose of genetic material carried by that excess chromosome causes malformation and mental retardation in the child.

✶ All through the 1920's and 1930's, many other such gross changes were studied and explained. Sometimes chromosomes break apart and repair themselves, but in the course of the repair one segment gets left out. Sometimes a segment gets attached to another chromosome, in effect duplicating a small section of its "message." There are circumstances in which chromosomes get tangled into loops and portions of them wind up in inverted order; and there are occasions when genetic material is exchanged between unlike chromosome pairs. Finally, there are changes in the composition of individual genes. All such changes, minor or major, are called mutations.

But before we discuss mutations as a research tool we should mention the geneticists' discovery, in the 1930's, that the chromosomes in the salivary glands of Drosophila larvae are 100 times larger than the chromosomes in ordinary body cells. Their detail is therefore correspondingly easier to see. Examination of such chromosomes revealed light and dark bandings that suggested flattish buttons stuffed into a tube. Were these bandings the genes? Experiments showed that given traits were controlled

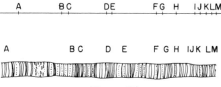

Figure 64

from specific sites on those chromosomes. And then the sites were compared with previously plotted genetic maps. They matched! (*See Figure 64.*) In addition, one could *see* crossing-over, breaks, loopings, and inversions. Thus, twenty years after Bridges' work, it was possible to probe a little deeper into the structures of the cell and for cytologists to confirm at a different level the findings based on the geneticists' breeding experiments.[1]

Now, to return to mutations.

One of the many miracles of life is that genetic changes occur with astounding rarity. During the years that members of the "Drosophila school" raised fruit flies by the hundreds of thousands, the number of mutants they found numbered only in the hundreds. Change is the exception; as a rule, genetic material is passed on from one generation to the next with fantastic precision.

The English chemist Francis H. C. Crick has estimated that if one could transcribe into written form all the instructions for making a man that are contained in his genes, and were to publish that "recipe" in as many 500-page books as were necessary to do the job, one would end up with close to a thousand volumes.

Suppose that such a work had been completed, and that a battery of competent typists was then given the job of copying the 500,000 pages in those volumes— not once, but twenty times. That's a total of 10,000,000 pages. How many typographical errors is it likely that they would make? Nobody knows, of course, but it is not

[1] In his *Heredity and Development,* John A. Moore appends this historical footnote: "The banding of salivary chromosomes in flies had been observed and recorded by cytologists before 1900, but this was not known to geneticists. If the Morgan group had been aware of this, their efforts would have been much easier. Their prediction of chromosomal aberrations . . . largely on genetic data was a tremendous intellectual achievement. All this time a simple method for demonstrating these cytological phenomena was buried and forgotten in the archives of biological literature. Cases such as this, which are not infrequent, make all scientists wonder what important facts have been discovered, forgotten, and now await rediscovery and a realization of their worth."

unreasonable to assume at least one typographical error per twenty pages of typing.

Compare now how the body does the same job of copying the instructions carried in the genes of a single human being. A cell that gives rise to sperms or egg cells may divide up to twenty or thirty times, at which point millions of cells will have been produced. And with each division the chromosomes make duplicates of themselves. Thus, they copy the equivalent of the 10,-000,000 pages assigned to those hypothetical typists—but they make *their* equivalent of a typographical error, a mutation, perhaps only every 1,000,000 pages!

Mutations affect an organism much as typographical errors affect the sense of what one is reading. Once in a great while an error can make an improvement—as when a fond father, wishing to buy riding breeches for a child, gives his secretary a handwritten memo specifying "jodphurs"; the typist gets her fingers tangled and writes "jodhpurs" on the order; and thus unwittingly corrects the spelling of the word. As we said earlier, the occasional "good" mutation—the kind that makes an organism function better—is the basis of evolution. But in general neither typographical errors nor mutations have beneficial effects.

A bad effect can be trivial, as in the omission of an unimportant letter. Writing "chromsomes" for "chromosomes" is comparable to a single-gene change with minor effects. The word still makes sense. Or the error can be so vast that utter nonsense results—as when one intends to type

Chromosomes are the threads of life.

but mistakenly places the fingers one key to the right of where they should be, producing

Vjtp,pdp,rd str yjr yjtrsfd pg ;ogr/

The only solution, then, is to eliminate it altogether.

The biological result of a completely garbled message is the same. A "genetic death" results. If the instructions that were garbled control a trait that is essential to the life of the organism—the way it makes blood, for example—the organism dies right away. If the instructions control a more superficial trait—the making of pigment, for instance, and albinism results—the organism dies on the installment plan: that is, it is more susceptible to disease, less fertile, produces fewer offspring, and in due course its "seed" vanishes from earth.

However, mutations are good for genetic research. Morgan's white-eyed flies, for example, were very useful as markers in tracing patterns of inheritance. And so the idea occurred to more than one investigator that if he could make more mutants in his laboratory than nature's fantastically accurate copying process normally provides, he would get farther faster in his study of genetics.

All kinds of approaches were used—heat, cold, churning, chemicals, pressure. But the normal low mutation rate of commonly used research plants or animals remained unchanged. Then, in 1926, the American biologist Herman J. Muller discovered that X-rays would do the trick. By irradiating huge batches of fruit flies, he produced 150 times as many mutations as normally occur. He got a veritable bazaar of new varieties, combinations of old ones, some cripples, and some corpses. Comparison of his irradiated flies with control groups that had not been irradiated showed that the X-rays had done everything from breaking chromosomes apart and recombining their segments to altering genes that controlled single traits.

Following his lead, other investigators X-rayed other organisms—corn, jimsonweed, tomatoes, mice, tobacco, wasps—and found that in them too the mutation rate increased fantastically. What's more, the man-made mutations were the same as natural ones. In Muller's flies, some of the deviations appeared that had turned up earlier in Morgan's lab. They behaved the same way, too: most were recessive; they reappeared in subsequent generations; and a high proportion of them had lethal effects.

Scientists were quick to realize that Muller had done much more than create a fresh supply of research material. He had increased mutation rates by applying massive doses of high-energy radiation—but *that* was only a matter of relativity; the basic principle he had demonstrated was that radiation induces mutation.

Nature's source of radiation is ultraviolet light, cosmic rays, or various radioactive elements in the earth and in the air. Here, then, was the probable source of some of those changes, great and small, which over the ages had modified—usually for the worse but occasionally for the better—the ability of living things to survive and reproduce themselves. Here, then, was raw material of evolution; the explanation in part of the origin of species!

There was no proof then—in the late twenties—as to exactly how radiation brings about genetic change. The assumption was that it alters the atomic structure of the gene and thus its behavior, much as a heart attack or a stroke changes the degree and kind of activity of which a human being is capable. But Muller's work indicated the direction in which genetic research should go. What is the structure of the gene? How does it function? Following chapters will supply some answers; but before we go on, a couple of comments about what has been written so far are in order.

None of these discoveries came tied together in neat chronological bundles. At any given period in the first quarter of the twentieth century there were always some unexplained facts lying around—as annoying, and as impossible to dispose of, as leftovers in a refrigerator. For example, the findings of cytology and those of the plant and animal breeders were usually out of phase; and it is only the long view of time that has made possible the step-by-step account you have just read. It is easier to understand that way, but it leaves the impression that what happened was sequential—like a relay race, in which a baton was passed hand to hand until a known goal was reached. While it was going on, it was in fact more like a game of marbles, with aggies and glassies and moonies shooting off in all directions.

A second flaw in the preceding chapters is that the diagrammatic sketches of cells and chromosomes are static. Try to think of them as stills taken from a motion picture, for that is what they properly are—a moment of motion "frozen" for detailed inspection, as in stop-watch photography. In life, the structural units of the cell are never really at rest. They undergo ceaseless chemical changes, each of which induces change else-where in the cell. The products of each change assume immediate new roles and elicit new responses; and thus make the cell a surging, dynamic system, always in flux.

It is the chemistry of the cell that will concern us from now on.

Chapter 14

SOME BIOCHEMICAL BEGINNINGS

This chapter is going to discuss, among other things, why roses are red and violets are blue; why Siamese cats and Shropshire sheep are born white but develop dark points; and why some people excrete black urine. It's also going to discuss how the souring of wine in France, the grinding-up of yeast cells in Germany, and the crystallization of jackbean juice in the United States helped scientists understand the chemistry of the genes.

But first let's understand what chemistry is. It is not the blending of liquids in beakers to see if something yellow turns green or something clear turns cloudy. Those are methods of investigation. Chemistry is the study of structure, properties, and reactions of substances.

As we said in the first chapter, all substances are made of atoms which are held together internally by electric forces. They join with each other to make molecules because they gain, lose, or share electrons in their outer shells. Of all kinds, carbon is what the mathematician Irving Adler calls "the most sociable atom" because it can join with other atoms in so many ways. Therefore, complexity of structure is an inherent possibility in carbon-containing molecules.

That the possibility has been well-realized by nature was early apparent. When eighteenth-century chemists began to have luck taking substances apart (the best way to learn how nature has put them together), they much more easily discovered the molecular structure of non-carbon-containing substances like water or of substances containing only a couple of carbon atoms, like ethyl alcohol, than of complex compounds like phenylalanine. (*Figure 65.*) In fact, the carbon-rich molecules of living organisms were such tough nuts to crack that the nine-

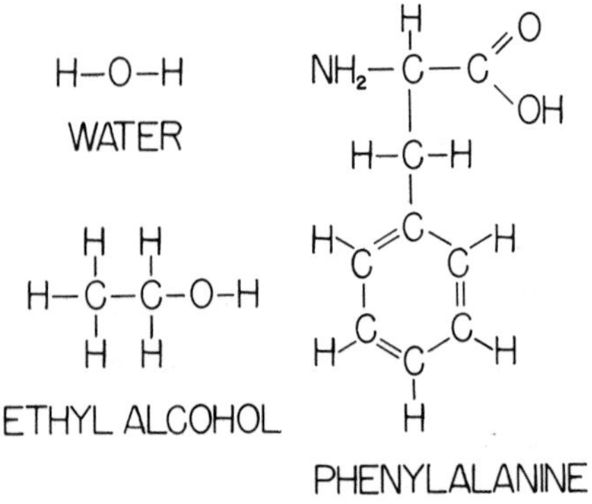

WATER	GLYCINE
ETHYL ALCOHOL	
PHENYLALANINE	TYROSINE

Figure 65 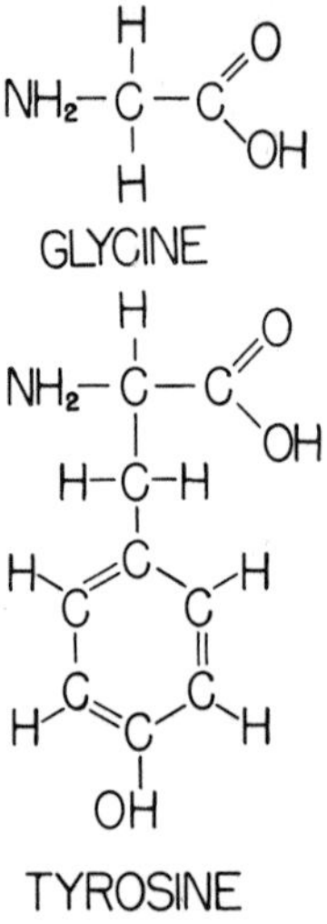   Figure 66

teenth century was well along before much progress was made.

A standard technique for loosening the bonds between atoms or groups of atoms is to apply heat to them, but it was learned in the eighteenth century that you don't get very far in using this method when studying a group of substances of which egg white is typical. Instead of becoming either more liquid or gaseous, such substances get more solid. So the application of heat was out.

Treating organic material with acid had worked well in breaking down starch and cellulose, both of which were known by 1820 to be composed of glucose (the sugar found in grapes). So the French chemist Braconnot gave the acid treatment to gelatin, a substance chemically like egg white. He got a sweet crystalline substance, but since further experiment showed that it contained nitrogen it couldn't be a sugar. He called it glycine. (The "-ine" suffix means "nitrogen-containing.)

Then he broke down muscle tissue the same way, and the white crystals he got that time—also nitrogen-containing—he called leucine. Somewhat later, the German chemist Justus von Liebig isolated a similar substance, from milk, which he called tyrosine. By then, the type of substances from which these products were derived had been labeled "proteins" (by the Dutch chemist Johannes Mulder). The products themselves, which were obviously components of proteins, were being called "amino acids." (*See Figure 66.*)

Glycine is the simplest amino acid. The other amino acids use it as a backbone, attaching to that center CH molecule a variety of individually different "side chains." It is through variation in the structure of side chains that each amino acid gets its individual properties. Compare, for example, glycine and tyrosine, and then look over at the sketch of phenylalanine in *Figure 65*. It, too, is an amino acid. Note that both it and tyrosine include a six-carbon ring formation.[1] This is properly called a benzene ring. The only difference between the two amino acids is that tyrosine has an atom of oxygen attached to its benzene ring, and phenylalanine does not.

That's enough for the moment about the structure of proteins—except to say that a nutritional lack of certain ones, or a malfunction in their formation within the body (since they are vital to blood, bone, nerve, and muscle) has swift and dire consequences to one's well being. Mulder recognized their importance when he named them. Protein means "of first rank."

By the end of the nineteenth century, organic chemists knew that proteins are giant molecules built of amino acids, and had identified many of those amino acids. (We now know that there are twenty kinds.) In 1907 the German chemist Emil Fischer managed to hook eighteen amino acids (of two kinds) into a long chain; and although what he got wasn't much of a protein, since those that occur in nature often contain 500 or more amino acids, it was a start toward understanding protein structure.

[1] In structural formulas like these, single lines represent one pair of shared electrons and double lines represent two pairs of shared electrons. This detail will not subsequently concern us, but you should be aware of its significance.

Many substances are naturally broken down into their component parts without any help from chemists. One such agent, known since earliest times, is yeast (which is a microscopic plant, one of the fungi). Pop it into bread dough and bubbles rise, lightening and raising the loaf. Pop it into grape juice and it breaks down the sugar in the juice, transforming it into alcohol. The process is called fermentation, and such agents as yeasts—agents which bring about decomposition of organic substances without themselves being changed—were long called "ferments." Science learned a good bit about their chemistry during the nineteenth century, in part because the French chemist Louis Pasteur was having a heated public argument with the German chemist Justus von Liebig, and each wanted to prove the correctness of his point of view.

Liebig had found the amino acid tyrosine, remember. He had also synthesized several organic substances. And in his opinion all that yeast and other organic ferments do is to produce chemicals that bring about decomposition. The fact that yeast is alive has nothing to do with its action, he said.

Liebig's belief was understandable. Industrial catalysts were then coming into use, and their action was clearly akin to that of the ferments—except that they were inorganic. Powdered nickel, for example, not only speeds up but is almost essential in the conversion of sulfur to sulfuric acid; and it is not itself altered in the process. The same is true of yet a third kind of chemical booster that was then beginning to be found—substances that were called "unorganized ferments" because they have an organic origin, but are not themselves alive. Among them were pepsin, a precipitate from the digestive juices of the stomach, and diastase, from malt, which converts starch to sugar. Since all three types of substances had the same effect, it is no wonder that Liebig considered them to be essentially alike.

Pasteur, on the other hand, said that the living ferments were a special case. Fermentation is a vital process of cell metabolism, he claimed: yeasts don't passively "produce chemicals" but initiate chemical changes in order to keep themselves alive. It is their robbing the glucose molecule in grape juice of oxygen that causes the conversion of grape sugar into alcohol. If one looks at wine-making from the yeasts' point of view, therefore, what happens to the grape juice is secondary. Its importance to them is that it provides them with the oxygen and energy needed for life.

Pasteur dramatized the relationship between the living state and fermentation when he helped France's wine industry avert a calamity. Wines were souring during aging. Why? Pasteur suggested that after the desired amount of fermentation had occurred the wine should be slowly heated to 135° F. to kill the yeasts. The idea of heating wine was a horrifying one, but the vintners were desperate. They tried the recommended "pasteurization" and found that it worked. (Nor have wine-drinkers been the sole beneficiaries of this discovery.)

When the German chemist Eduard Büchner pounded some yeast cells to bits, in 1897, and found that the residue—which certainly couldn't be called alive—was still capable of causing fermentation, scientists realized that there was no essential difference between ferments in living and disintegrated cells, and gave them a joint name: enzymes.

Liebig was right, because they do for organic compounds exactly what the industrial catalysts do for inorganic compounds. They make reactions go faster that would otherwise barely proceed. But Pasteur was right, too. When living organisms such as yeasts cause chemical changes in other substances they do it as a sideline to their own imperative of maintaining life.

In 1918, the German chemist Otto Meyerhof discovered that animal cells (in muscle) and plant cells (in yeast) break down the sugar which is the source of their energy in precisely the same way. Thus he proved that enzyme action is essential to the cell metabolism of all living things.

But what about the chemistry of enzymes themselves?

During the early decades of the twentieth century, it was mostly a case of theorizing:

1. In 1902, the German chemist George Lunge suggested that enzymes bring about chemical changes by functioning as middlemen in the cell; that is, by passing on to one molecule a needed atom or group of atoms and *at the same time* seizing from another molecule a replacement for themselves. Such close coordination of action could explain why organic catalysts make reactions go faster.

2. In 1916, the American Irving Langmuir suggested that enzymes may accomplish the speedup by actually (if temporarily) affixing themselves to the substance they are about to catalyze. This they certainly couldn't do unless they were shaped somehow to fit its surface pattern—any more than dogs' paws will fit into human gloves.

Langmuir's theory made sense because it was known that enzymes are highly specific; that is, they react with just one substance (or with several chemically closely related substances). This specificity is easy to visualize at the molecular level if you think of each enzyme as having atoms that project outward, say, in the same position where molecules of the substance to be catalyzed have indentations. It's much the same design principle that makes a particular key fit a particular lock.

3. The third theory, for which there wasn't much proof during the early years of the century, was that enzymes are proteins.

And all three theories were correct. The one that is most important to this narrative is the third. Proof for the protein nature of enzymes didn't come until 1926–1935, when the American James B. Sumner isolated and crystallized an enzyme from jackbeans and John Howard Northrop did the same with pepsin and other enzymes, and established the chemical composition of these substances by the use of tests not available in the early decades of the century.

And what did any of the foregoing have to do with the infant science of genetics? Very little—*then*. The reason was that geneticists and chemists didn't know they were investigating the same subject. They were like those legendary blind men, each of whom felt a different part of the elephant and concluded that the part he had felt was the whole beast.

Morgan and others were completely absorbed in what they were learning about the *mechanisms* of inheritance. In talking about "the gene for brown eyes," they knew of course that the gene didn't have brown eyes, didn't pass on to the cell any brown pigment, and therefore must carry information that told the cell how to *make* brown eyes. But what the process was, nobody knew; and hardly anybody knew how to do more than speculate about it.

As for the chemists, they couldn't take genetics very seriously. Geneticists spent all their time taking inventories. Raising bottles full of fruit flies, keeping pedigrees on rabbits, laboriously hand-pollinating corn and then counting the kernels . . . none of this seemed, somehow, to be real science. The words of the botanist John Merle Coulter, writing in 1912, were still true: "Now the Mendelians constitute a conspicuous biological cult, and Mendelism has extended from its simple original statement into a speculative philosophy, with conceptions of unit-characters, dominance, ratios, etc. that the untrained cannot follow."[2]

Happily, there were a few exceptions to this split between the two disciplines. Plant pigments had value as dyestuffs, and their chemistry excited interest—if only for the prosaic reason of synthesizing them—even before 1900. It also became evident very early that plant coloration is inherited according to Mendelian laws. So there was slightly more communication between scientists interested in understanding pigmentation than between those who were charting chromosome maps in fruit flies, say, and those who were trying to crack the protein molecule in blood.

In the years between 1905 and 1913, a number of

[2] From *Heredity and Eugenics*, by W. E. Castle, J. M. Coulter, C. B. Davenport, E. M. East, and W. L. Tower (Chicago: University of Chicago Press, 1912).

investigators—notably the German chemist Richard Will-stätter—managed to crystallize the pigments responsible for making roses red and violets blue (by such devices as bruising the petals of pelargoniums and cornflowers, then processing them with weak solutions of acid and ether).[3] Among the interesting facts that emerged from such research was that all plants with coloration in the red–purple range have essentially the same pigment molecule and that the expressed color is a reaction of the pigment molecule to alkalinity or acidity in the cell sap. It makes bright red pigment in the presence of acid, violet in a neutral solution, and deep purple when the environment is alkaline.

Temperature, light, and the presence of certain minerals were also found to affect coloration. There is a kind of corn, for instance, which has husks striped in red and green; and the striping corresponds to the amount of growth that takes place in daylight and the amount that takes place at night. A corollary in the animal kingdom is the light and dark barring of feathers in Plymouth Rock chickens. And what about the temperature sensitivity of the Himalayan rabbit, the Shropshire sheep, the Siamese cat? All are born white, and then develop pigment at the extremities, where the body is coolest.

Yet all these color variations were known to be inherited. Could it be that *genes* create or respond to conditions of alkalinity or acidity, or to differences in temperature or light? What about their apparent specificity? The more that people studied pigmentation, the clearer it became that exceedingly slight variations in color or effect were under genetic control. Do genes do more than just "carry information"? Are they, perhaps, active agents of chemical change?

[3] Chemically, there are many different kinds of plant and animal pigments. Plant pigments in the red–purple range are easiest to study because they can be dissolved in water. The green pigment of chlorophyll (fat-soluble) was more difficult to understand. And the animal pigment, melanin, was understood only recently because it's practically *in*soluble. An old scientific joke goes this way: "Dissolve a horse, and what's left is melanin."

An English physician, Sir Archibald Garrod, thought so. He was interested in inherited diseases (which he called "inborn errors of metabolism"), and in 1909 he published a book in which he discussed in detail a disease called alkaptonuria. A great deal was known about the chemistry of this disease, because its major symptom—the blackening of urine on explosure to air—is so striking that it had been much studied. It's a rare disease, has no particularly bad effects until late in life, but is (to say the least) disturbing. The villain is alkapton, also known as homogentisic acid, which is excreted in excessive amounts in the urine of affected individuals. This ought not to happen: normal individuals break it down into acetoacetic acid.

Each reaction in the metabolic chain has a House-that-Jack-Built relationship to a preceding reaction, so: acetoacetic acid is a product of homogentisic acid; homogentisic acid is a product (via several stages) of tyrosine; and tyrosine is (or can be) a product of phenylalanine. Those last two are amino acids, remember; and *they* come from protein. Specifically, from meat or eggs eaten at dinner, which are then broken down by the digestive enzymes of the stomach, so that the cells of the body can use their components to form blood, muscle, bones, nerves, and so on.

At this point you should be beginning to see how the sections of this chapter fit together.

The main difference between acetoacetic acid and all its precursors is that they include the benzene ring we called to your attention in connection with *Figures 65* and *66*, and acetoacetic acid does not. To make it from its precursor homogentisic acid, the benzene ring must be split apart—something that alkaptonurics cannot do. There is a roadblock in their metabolic system at the point where normal people convert homogentisic acid into acetoacetic acid.

Garrod had studied medical literature and the pedigrees of people afflicted with alkaptonuria, and he discussed these family histories with the geneticist Bateson. There didn't seem to be much doubt that alkaptonuria is inherited as a simple Mendelian recessive. That is, if A is the gene controlling the ability to split the benzene ring in homogentisic acid, the defective form would be a. In an individual with aa genes, then, the chemical chain would be broken at the point where the body makes homogentisic acid.

But what specific agent broke the chain? Garrod's theory—and a brilliantly intuitive one—was that "the splitting of the benzene ring of homogentisic acid in normal metabolism is the work of a special enzyme, and in congenital alkaptonuria this enzyme is wanting." He didn't actually say that a defective gene was responsible for the absence of his "special enzyme," but the cause-and-effect relationship was clearly implicit in his writings.

He made research use of alkaptonurics by feeding them compounds that were thought to be precursors of homogentisic acid; discovered that the amount excreted had a quantitative relationship to the amount ingested; and thus initiated a now widely used method for determining whether one compound is a metabolic precursor of another. Checking the chemicals excreted is a valuable medical tool for understanding which link in a metabolic chain has snapped.

Garrod's work represents the beginning of both modern biochemical genetics and medical genetics—but it was a "beginning" like that of a ball game in which someone pitches a ball and no one returns it. Although his work was mentioned by Bateson in a 1913 book about heredity, and Garrod's own book was reprinted in 1923, the record of his work was subsequently lost in the dim recesses of libraries. Biochemists weren't interested in genetics and geneticists weren't interested in biochemistry.

It wasn't until the mid-1930's that interpretations similar to Garrod's grew out of further research into the chemistry of pigmentation. He was rescued from obscurity by the English geneticist J. B. S. Haldane, who pointed out in 1942 that discoveries about gene-enzyme relationships which were then being touted as new had in fact been anticipated by Garrod, thirty years earlier.

Chapter 15

FLIES' EYES AND BREAD MOLD

By the early 1930's, it was increasingly clear that genes control development and that development is a process involving a series of enzyme-controlled chemical reactions. But how do genes control enzymes—if they do? Geneticists and biochemists were like miners tunneling toward each other in the dark. Would they effect a junction, or were the routes they were following going to bypass each other at different levels?

One logical site for the study of development was the embryo; but, alas, the embryologists' favorite sea urchins or frogs couldn't be grown by the millions in half-pint milk bottles, and the geneticists' favorite fruit flies were so small that only madmen would attempt the finicky microsurgery required to study their embryonic development. Hence, although much was known about the genetics of fruit flies and the embryology of frogs, little was known vice versa. It would certainly be a step in the right direction if someone could acquire equally detailed information about the genetics and the embryonic development of the *same* organism. . . .

In 1935 the Russian-born biologist Boris Ephrussi and the American biologist George W. Beadle, then at Caltech, joined forces in a laboratory in Paris—determined to have a try at closing this gap. Since the genetics of the fruit fly were so well understood, they decided to be madmen and explore its embryology. To attempt dissection of larvae only 1/10th of an inch long was formidable in itself, but when they told a noted authority on insect development that they proposed to transplant the embryonic beginnings of organs from one larva to another, and asked for his advice, he was succinct: "Forget about it." Although the embryonic "buds" on fruit fly larvae eventually grow into well-differentiated parts in the adult, he said, one organ is hardly distinguishable from another while in bud form.

But Ephrussi and Beadle were young and optimistic. They spent months teasing Drosophila larvae into place under a microscope; removing embryonic buds with microscalpels; holding them in micropipettes; easing them into the body cavities of other larvae; and hoping that the transplant would grow in the body of its host. Mostly, it didn't; but there came a day when one of the host larvae *did* mature. It was a fly with three eyes. So that bud had been an eye bud! More importantly, the transplantation technique was feasible. Now, the two men asked themselves, what shall we do with it?

They remembered the unresolved riddle of vermilion eyes in gynandromorphs, a story that goes this way:

Among the oddities that had turned up in the fly bottles of Morgan and other members of the Drosophila school of research were flies that were partly male and partly female. These mixed-up creatures—which are called gynandromorphs—sometimes had heads with a red eye on one side and a white eye on the other, one wing of a type normally found in a female and one of a type normally found in a male, and other combinations of traits that indicated the presence in the fly of *both* XX and XY genetic directions. What had happened?

In time it was discovered that flies of this type had started out as females—that is, as XX fertilized eggs; but with one of the early cell divisions, one of the daughter cells failed to get the two X chromosomes it should have received (*see Figure 67*). The genetic constitution of that deprived cell was therefore the same as if it had inherited the single X chromosome of an XY egg, and it became "male." As embryonic growth continued, cells of this single-X character multiplied at the same rate as those of the sister XX cell and eventually developed into an adult with tissue of two kinds (*see Figure 68*). Unaffected equally by the genetic composition of adjacent tissues or by the presence in the same organism of cells carrying different directions for the same trait, each kind of cell faithfully carried out its own genetic directions,

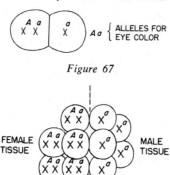

Figure 67

FEMALE TISSUE   MALE TISSUE

Figure 68

even if the resulting fly had one red eye and one white eye (or other anomalies).

There were some exceptions to this rule of independence. Among them was the mutant eye-color vermilion, which is sex-linked. A. H. Sturtevant (whose work on chromosome maps was described in Chapter 13) had discovered that those gynandromorphs whose eyes arise from male tissue and therefore should have been vermilion have dark red eyes instead, the color characteristic of normal flies and in these instances characteristic of female tissue in the gynandromorph. Why the color change?

The action of hormones—which diffuse through the body from the glands that manufacture them, but which have highly specific effects on development—was known, hence it occurred to Sturtevant that this might be an analogous situation. Perhaps some diffusible substance moved from the female part of the fly's body to the eyes in male tissue and caused them to make the brown pigment which is the difference between the bright red of vermilion and the dark red that is normal.

Ephrussi and Beadle decided to see whether this color change occurred only in gynandromorphs or whether it was common to normal flies, too. Now that they knew which embryonic bud in a Drosophila larva would grow into an eye, they transplanted eye buds from vermilion flies into larvae from dark red-eye stock; and, sure enough, the vermilion transplants matured into red eyes in the adult. Subsequently, another eye-color trait—cinnabar— was found to behave in the same way. In each case, *something* in the host increased pigmentation in the transplanted eyes.

The next step was to use the two mutants, vermilion and cinnabar, in reciprocal transplants. The two investigators expected that each transplant would take on the coloration natural to its host, vermilion developing as cinnabar and cinnabar as vermilion; *or* that both transplants would develop as dark red eyes. But neither expectation was realized. Cinnabar eyes in vermilion hosts remained cinnabar, and vermilion eyes in cinnabar hosts turned dark red.

It didn't make sense. Unless . . . Yes, it *would* make sense if one assumed that two different substances were necessary to normal red-eye pigmentation, one convertible to the other.

What if substance A were an essential precursor of substance B; substance B were an essential precursor of normal red-eye pigment; and deviations from dark red represented blockages in this normal chain of events? Suppose that at the point in the chain where an enzyme should form substance A, a mutant gene interrupted the reaction and pigment formation stopped at that point, giving a vermilion eye? Suppose that the reaction went a step farther so that the fly could make substance A, but a mutant gene prevented the making of substance B, and the result of *that* blockage was a cinnabar eye? (*See Figure 69.*)

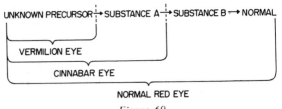

Figure 69

Thus, a cinnabar eye implanted in a vermilion host would find itself in an organism with less capability for making pigment than it already had, and the eyes would develop as cinnabar. In contrast, a vermilion eye implanted in a cinnabar host would now have a supply of substance A—with which it could proceed to make substance B and thus develop with dark red eyes.

If Ephrussi and Beadle had known about Garrod, or had explored scientific literature more thoroughly, they would have seen that they had a case of blocked reactions similar to the one that Garrod had described for alkaptonuria. But Garrod had not yet been rediscovered. So they struggled on, one in France and the other in California, trying to answer two fundamental questions:

1. Did any of the 26 other mutant eye-color genes then known in Drosophila behave like vermilion and cinnabar?

The answer was "no." The two biologists investigated all 26 mutants, and satisfied themselves that the chain of chemical reactions they had postulated was unique. Thus, they added an additional small bit of evidence to the geneticists' growing belief that each gene has only *one* primary job, and that job is to direct *one* chemical reaction.

2. What is the chemical nature of substances A and B?

They couldn't find out. They discovered that the "unknown precursor" in the diagram above is an amino acid called tryptophane, but at that point they got stuck. Nor did the subsequent collaboration of G. W. Beadle and the American chemist Edward L. Tatum—both of whom, by the late 1930's, were at Stanford—get the investigation much farther forward.

By 1940, Beadle and Tatum had given up on eye pigmentation in fruit flies and had decided that there must be a better organism for studying the chemistry of inherited abnormalities. But what was it? The familiar stumbling block was still there: too little was known about the chemistry of organisms that were understood genetically. If the two men picked another genetic trait and tried to work out *its* chemistry, their chances were good of finding themselves again on a dead-end street.

The logical alternative, they then decided, was to reverse the procedure they'd been following. They had been trying to discover the particular chemical reactions particular genes directed. Why not find an organism whose chemical reactions were well known; irradiate it and (with luck) induce mutations that would block specific reactions; and thus (with luck) identify the genes that controlled those reactions?

The organism they finally decided to use was as commonplace and as domesticated as the fruit fly (and was destined to become almost as famous a research tool). It was the red bread mold *Neurospora* (pronounced New-ROS-por-a) *crassa*. It wasn't quite the ideal organism that the two scientists had dreamed of, for although its life cycle is brief, it can be grown in vast quantities in the laboratory, and its genetics was extremely well known, no one was certain what its basic nutritional requirements were. Since Beadle and Tatum proposed to interfere with its metabolic processes, this information was essential.

Actually, they weren't in much danger of finding themselves on another chemical dead-end street, because the nutritional requirements of similar molds *were* well known, and they had only to compare Neurospora with its cousins. Tatum did it by determining the irreducible minimum of raw materials required by the mold. He grew it on media which were progressively poorer in amino acids, sugars, vitamins, and other sources of nourishment, and eventually located its nutritional threshold of life. It *has* to have certain inorganic salts, a source of carbon, a source of energy such as sucrose, and one vitamin—biotin.

(Incidentally, the two investigators were very lucky in their timing. Biotin had recently been discovered, and had just become available to them for laboratory use. If they had tried only a year or two earlier to grow Neurospora on the various synthetic media that their experiment envisaged, they would have been unable to do so.)

With this one piece of missing information acquired, Beadle and Tatum were ready to proceed.

Neurospora is a very resourceful plant. It can reproduce in a variety of ways. It comes in two mating types, so-called because they are alike in appearance and therefore cannot appropriately be called sexes. Both mating types have only one set of seven chromosomes in their nuclei. They readily reproduce asexually through fragmentation of the mold filaments (hyphae), or by special asexual spores. Also, however, in a process akin to the union of eggs and sperm in higher plants and animals, the nuclei of the two mating types can fuse to form double nuclei with two sets of chromosomes.

These double nuclei, each in a cell that will become a spore sac, first undergo *meiotic* division (the kind characteristic of sex cells in higher organisms). Next, each nucleus reproduces by *mitosis* (the duplication characteristic of ordinary body cells in higher organisms). The result is eight sexual spores, each of which contains a nucleus with only *one* of each pair of chromosomes and is capable of growing into a mold colony of one or the other of the two mating types.

In the example depicted in *Figure 70,* you have to visualize all seven pairs of chromosomes and the multitude of alternative traits they carry. We are tracing the genetic history of only one pair of traits—the two alleles that make Neurospora grow in thin web-like filaments (A) or in compact clusters (a).

This is a convenient arrangement for an investigator because *all* the products of meiosis mature (in animals, remember, only one in four egg cells matures); and all are kept handily packaged in the ascus. Furthermore, he can readily tell, from each spore's location in the chain of eight, whether a hybrid gene pair was segregated in the first or second of the two meiotic cell divisions. Finally, he has a duplicate of each of the four that were formed during these divisions.

If he is a very careful worker, with steady hands and much patience, he can open an ascus (using a microscope and a thin glass needle, inasmuch as each spore is only

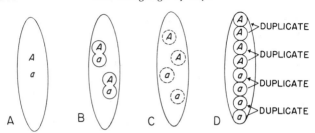

A. *Parent cell. After the mating type A fuses with mating type a to create a hybrid individual, a sac-like structure called an ascus forms around the cell.*

B. *First sex-cell division. Then meiosis takes place. In a crosswise split like the halving of a biscuit, two duplicates of the parental cell are formed.*

C. *Second sex-cell division. Next, these two cells divide, the A's and the a's segregating in the classic 1:1 ratio.*

D. *Duplication. Finally, by mitosis (ordinary cell division), each of the four about-to-be spores makes an exact duplicate of itself; and cell walls form around each of the eight.*

Figure 70

1/1000th of an inch long) and can transfer the spores into test tubes in the same order in which they were lined up in the ascus. As the spores germinate, their genetic attributes tell the story of which genes went where when the initial cell divided. Thus, one can work out the pedigrees of bread mold quite as exactly as those of fruit flies.

But don't forget that each plant can reproduce asexually. Tips of hyphae become segmented, each segment becoming a spore which in genetic constitution is a faithful copy of the spore from which the whole plant colony grew. These reproduce by the simple process of duplication that is characteristic of all body cells except sex cells. Therefore, once you know the genetic makeup of any given Neurospora plant, you can grow as many duplicates as suits your research needs. Doing so is like making cuttings of a geranium plant or multiple prints from the same photographic negative.

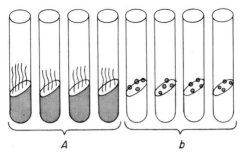

*These test tubes, which represent secondary cultures repro-
duced asexually, show that genes controlling two patterns of
growth have segregated 1:1 during sex-cell division.*

Figure 71

Beadle and Tatum started out by subjecting quantities
of asexual spores to X-rays, to induce mutations. These
were then crossed with strains that had not been irradiated, and the resultant spores were picked out of the
ascus of each plant and raised in test tubes. The nutrient
medium supplied for them to grow on was super-rich in
amino acids and vitamins, so that a mutant strain unable
to make one of them for itself would find what it needed
in the medium and would survive for use in phase two
of the experiment.

Then, after these plants had matured, asexual spores
were transferred to test tubes containing a medium that
provided nothing but the inorganic salts, the carbon, the
sugar, and the one vitamin, biotin, that are the mold's
minimum nutritional requirement. If a mold that could
ordinarily grow in such a medium could not do so after
it had been irradiated, Beadle and Tatum felt safe in
predicting that the reason would be a genetic mutation
which blocked one or more steps in a series of chemical
reactions.

But with what frequency would mutations occur? They
had no idea. They were afraid that the frequency might
be so low that they'd get discouraged and quit before they
found one, so they made a pact: they'd isolate and grow
1000 different plants (from sexual spores) before they

made any growth-tests (with asexual spores) on the minimal medium.

As it turned out, they hit pay dirt at number 299. This, their first mutant, couldn't grow on the minimal medium because it had lost the ability to make vitamin B-6. (They found the point of blockage by returning the same spores to the minimal growing medium and then, one by one, adding the various supplements.)

Their second mutant—they were into the second thousand by then, its number being 1085—couldn't make vitamin B-1. This time they agreed not to quit until they had ten mutants. Before long, they had hundreds. And some interesting facts had emerged.

Among their investigative group at Stanford was a young geneticist named Adrian Srb (now at Cornell). Srb found three mutants that had lost their ability to make the amino acid arginine. One of them—call it A^1— would grow only if arginine was added directly to its nutrient medium. Another—A^2—would grow if it got either arginine or another amino acid, citrulline. The third—A^3—would grow if it got arginine, citrulline, or a third amino acid, ornithine.

Remembering the chain of chemical reactions that Beadle and Ephrussi had postulated to account for the pigmentation of vermilion and cinnabar eyes in fruit flies, it was now possible to draw a similar diagram for Neurospora's manufacture of arginine (*see Figure 72*):

If each of these steps were directed by an enzyme and the enzyme were in turn controlled by a gene, the diagram would indicate that irradiation had destroyed the A^3 gene, and therefore that particular Neurospora

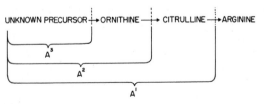

Figure 72

strain couldn't make the enzyme which converts the unknown precursor into ornithine. Given ornithine, the genes and enzymes controlling the manufacture of citrulline and arginine could function, of course. So, too, with the A^2 gene: its destruction deprived the mold of the enzyme that transforms ornithine into citrulline. But if it were to obtain citrulline as a dietary supplement, its normal A^1 gene and enzyme could finish the job of making arginine. Finally, if the A^1 gene had been knocked out, nothing but arginine itself would repair the damage in that particular strain of Neurospora.

All this seemed proof enough that each chemical reaction is controlled by just one gene and through it by one enzyme. But it was possible to be even more sure. The final step by Beadle and Tatum was to cross each of these mutants with their normal counterparts, and check the characteristics of the resulting spores in each ascus. If, in the final set of test tubes, four spores were always normal and four were always mutant, this 1:1 ratio would indicate that only a single gene had changed.

The excitement of the two scientists, as they watched the spores germinate, was comparable to Mendel's as he split open pods that he hoped would contain the kind of peas he had predicted. And with few exceptions, *their* predictions were correct, too. The batteries of test tubes consistently yielded four normals and four mutants. It followed, of course, that if a one-gene mutation prevented the making of the enzyme that directed one particular step in a chain of chemical reactions, that each reaction in that chain must be controlled by one gene. This is called the one-gene, one-enzyme theory.

What Beadle and Tatum had done was to discover the hard way what Garrod had discovered thirty-eight years before. But they had gone far beyond his single example of an "inborn error of metabolism," alkaptonuria, and had demonstrated so many instances of gene-controlled, enzymatically activated reactions in a living organism that their conclusions were impossible to ignore. Additionally, the time was ripe: by 1941, when they published their results, geneticists and biochemists were ready to pull in tandem. Today, it's hard to tell one from the other.

An inherited metabolic disease in man that has been understood only in recent years is phenylketonuria (PKU), which is much more serious than alkaptonuria because children who have it become feebleminded. PKU is caused by a gene-enzyme defect that causes excessive amounts of phenylpyruvic acid to build up in the body, where it is toxic to the central nervous system. Babies' blood, or their urine in diapers, can now be tested for the presence of this acid; if treatment is begun soon after birth the disease can be circumvented and normal or near-normal mentality assured.

Galactosemia is another inborn error of metabolism. It is caused by the lack of a gene and therefore of the enzyme which enables a baby to convert galactose sugar in milk to a usable form. Untreated, it causes damage to brain, eyes, and liver.

Still another metabolic disease—although it's not commonly thought of as a "disease"—is albinism, the condition that expresses itself as pink eyes and white hair in men, mice, rabbits, and many other creatures. An albino is incapable of making melanin, the pigment that colors animal hair or skin. Melanin derives from the amino acids tyrosine or phenylalanine. At a halfway-point in the pigment-making chain, a gene-enzyme defect blocks conversion of these substances into melanin. Pink eyes result because there is no pigment to obscure the color of the blood vessels in the retina. Additionally, albinos are exceedingly light-sensitive, because melanin screens out excessive radiation and they lack its protection.

But perhaps the most elegantly researched mystery of genetic disease is the Case of the Sickle Cells in hemoglobin.

The story begins, interestingly enough, just about the time that Garrod published his findings on alkaptonuria. In 1910, a Chicago doctor noticed that the red blood cells of a young Negro patient had a sickle shape instead of the normal round shape. Such cells are unable to carry enough oxygen, die quickly, and thus cause anemia in the patient.

If *Aa* is the gene controlling the formation of red blood cells and an individual inherits *A* from one parent and *a* from the other, the normal *A* will direct the making of enough normal hemoglobin so the defective *a* will have no effect—unless exceptional deprivation of oxygen occurs (as when climbing Mount Everest; people with this inheritance had better stay nearer sea level). A person with *Aa* inheritance is described medically as having sickle-cell trait. But if he has inherited both defective genes—*aa*—he has sickle-cell disease, and often dies in childhood.

Once this disease had been described, many physicians found it in their patients, and noted that it appears almost entirely in Negroes. Why? And if in its pure form it is lethal, why does it persist in the population? We now know that it is caused by a mutant gene which either arose in equatorial Africa or was brought there by Asian peoples who migrated to Africa thousands of years ago. It has persisted in Africa because it was a "good" mutation: for some reason, people of *Aa* constitution have higher resistance to malaria than those with *aa* constitution (who usually die of anemia) or those with *AA* constitution (who are likely to die of malaria). In a malaria-ridden part of the world, therefore, it is an *advantage* to have sickle-cell trait. Approximately 25 per cent of natives of some parts of central Africa have it.

In the United States, however, less than 9 per cent of Negroes are affected. This reveals two facts about inheritance: that mutations are not in themselves either good or bad, but give an individual an advantage or not within the context of his environment; and that it takes a very long time for a defective gene to work its way out of a population. The sickle-cell gene came to the United States with the eighteenth-century slave ships; in the absence of malaria and in the presence of other genes for making hemoglobin it is slowly dying out through the process of Darwinian natural selection.

The biochemistry of sickle-cell hemoglobin (S-hemo-globin) was worked out by the American chemist Linus Pauling and his collaborators in 1949. It is one of a number of hemoglobins, all of which apparently are mutants of the same two genes, one for each of the two protein chains of the hemoglobin molecule. The British biochemist V. M. Ingram found the nature of the chain in C- and S-hemoglobin by using an involved and delicate method of investigation. It began with the breakdown of three kinds of hemoglobin—A, C, and S—into the chains of amino acids that are called peptides, followed by the separation of these peptides into their constituent amino acids. Here's how one of the several peptide chains is built:

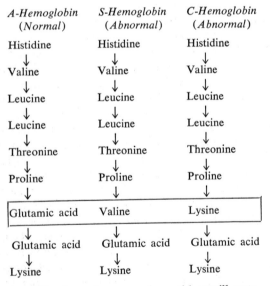

A-Hemoglobin *(Normal)*	*S-Hemoglobin* *(Abnormal)*	*C-Hemoglobin* *(Abnormal)*
Histidine	Histidine	Histidine
↓	↓	↓
Valine	Valine	Valine
↓	↓	↓
Leucine	Leucine	Leucine
↓	↓	↓
Leucine	Leucine	Leucine
↓	↓	↓
Threonine	Threonine	Threonine
↓	↓	↓
Proline	Proline	Proline
↓	↓	↓
Glutamic acid	Valine	Lysine
↓	↓	↓
Glutamic acid	Glutamic acid	Glutamic acid
↓	↓	↓
Lysine	Lysine	Lysine

These differ by only one amino acid, you'll note.

One gene. One enzyme. One amino acid. Never let it be said that one unit of anything is unimportant.

Chapter 16

SECRETS OF LIFE IN LILLIPUT

Bacteria are old acquaintances of man. The first of them to be identified, in 1773, were the rod-shaped bacilli and the spiral spirilli. By the mid-nineteenth century, the German botanist F. J. Cohn had described and classified so many kinds and had done such monumental research into their nature that he is called the founder of modern bacteriology.

But the most significant discovery about bacteria (at least from the human viewpoint) was made by Pasteur in 1865, when he identified them as causative agents of disease.

You will remember that Pasteur's discoveries about the chemistry of enzymes grew out of his efforts to prevent the souring of wine. Likewise, this second great discovery was the by-product of efforts to save another French industry from disaster. In the 1860's, a mysterious epidemic was killing off French silkworms, thus threatening the silk industry with extinction. Pasteur found that bacteria were the cause, and from that beginning formulated his "germ theory of disease"—one of the major milestones of medicine.

THE 3 MAIN TYPES OF BACTERIA

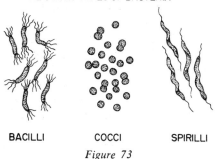

BACILLI   COCCI   SPIRILLI

Figure 73

Ever since then, bacteria—sometimes called "germs," sometimes called "microbes," sometimes called by their own proper surnames—have been the object of intense interest. Different bacteria have, over the years, been identified as the infective agents in tuberculosis, syphilis, pneumonia, scarlet fever, lockjaw, and typhoid fever. The biggest bacterium is perhaps 1/5000th of an inch in diameter, and they grade down to specks that are about 1/25,000th of an inch in diameter. Man has learned to defend himself against these tiny enemies by killing them with chemicals or by subverting them to work against their own interests, as they do in a vaccine.

Among the early chemical approaches was the English surgeon Lister's technique of pouring carbolic acid on a wound (which, unfortunately, destroyed the surrounding tissue as well as the bacteria). Today, in addition to such external techniques as a well-scrubbed Dr. Kildare, surgically sterilized tools, and a dusting of antibiotic in the open wound, bacterial diseases are attacked by dosing a patient with drugs which move into the bloodstream and destroy the bacteria by interfering with their metabolism. Sulfa was the first of such drugs, in 1932.

Vaccination originated as a defense against smallpox.[1] In the eighteenth century, when smallpox was the scourge of humanity, country people in Gloucestershire deliberately infected themselves with cowpox, hoping that the light illness that usually resulted would confer immunity against the dreaded smallpox. (This is an example of the wisdom inherent in some folk remedies.) An English physician, Edward Jenner, refined the technique, and developed the first smallpox vaccine.

But it was Louis Pasteur who gave us our basic modern methods. Pasteur was indeed a darling of the gods: what he didn't accomplish as a result of brilliant intellectual insight, he stumbled onto as a result of lucky chance. In this case, he was testing cultures of the bacteria that cause cholera in chickens, and happened to use a culture

[1] Which we now know is caused by a virus, not by bacteria. More about viruses shortly.

that had been standing in his lab so long it had lost its potency. The chickens got sick, but recovered. In an effort to correct his "mistake," Pasteur then injected them with a fresh, full-strength culture. This time they didn't even get sick.

No happier mistake has ever been made, for the discovery that the virulence of bacteria can be attenuated is the basis of modern vaccines. An injection of weakened or heat-killed bacteria does not cause the disease but *does* stimulate the formation in the blood of protein substances called antibodies. These have such chemical affinity for the bacteria that caused their formation that in the event of subsequent infection they combine with the invading bacteria, throw them out of gear, and thus render them impotent.

One can be vaccinated against many virus diseases, too. But men didn't know much about viruses before the 1930's beyond the fact that *something* other than identifiable bacteria caused malaria, yellow fever, polio, measles, mumps, influenza, and the common cold (in man); and rabies, hoof-and-mouth disease, and psittacosis in animals.

And these somethings were obviously incredibly small: not only were they invisible to the eye or to a microscope but in liquid suspensions they squeezed right through the holes in materials intended to filter them out but allow the liquid to pass through. (That's why for many years they were called "filterable viruses." The word virus, incidentally, means "poison.")

Pasteur's contention that viruses are "germs" essentially no different from the bacteria he knew so well—only smaller—was a simple and appealing explanation. But science dislikes the postulation of invisible things as an explanation of observed phenomena (as witness Mendel's difficulty in persuading members of the Brünn Society for the Study of Natural Science that genes exist). Until somebody *saw* a virus, or overwhelming indirect evidence was amassed in support of the theory that they are "germs," there would be doubt.

Contrary evidence came in the 1930's.

There is a disease that mottles tobacco leaves and

thus destroys their value as a crop. It was work done on this disease in the nineteenth century, in fact, that established the possible existence of infective agents smaller than bacteria; and since then tobacco mosaic virus has been so much studied that it often goes by its initials, TMV.

In 1935, the American biochemist Wendell Stanley mashed up some diseased leaves and processed them in an attempt to get the virus in as pure and concentrated form as possible. He wound up with a crystalline powder which appeared as inert as sugar or salt, but when later dissolved in liquid had as much ability to cause infection as the diseased tobacco leaves from which it had been obtained.

Stanley's discovery seemed to prove that the unseen particles called viruses were not "germs" or any other living organism. If there was one thing that science was sure of, it was that the rigidly set patterns of crystalline substances had nothing in common with the flexible, ever-changing patterns of the living cell. If TMV could be crystallized but still be infectious, surely TMV—and, by extension, other viruses—couldn't be alive in the same sense that bacteria were.

But after healthy tobacco leaves had been deliberately infected with a minute amount of Stanley's crystallized-and-then-revitalized TMV, the disease spread. More TMV could be crystallized from this second generation of infected plants. Isn't the ability to grow and reproduce as standard a measure of life as crystallinity is a measure of non-life? It was very puzzling.

Viruses are so small relative to the wave lengths of visible light that it "flows" right around them; that's why they cannot be seen in a microscope that uses visible light. What first made viruses "visible" was the electron microscope, invented in 1937. Electrons can be concentrated into a beam which *is* stopped by particles as small as viruses, and leaves a record of that stoppage on a photographic plate.

In 1944, the availability of this new tool plus experience gained in observing the far reaches of outer space were applied to the world of lilliputian life on earth, and the mystery of the viruses began to be solved. The American astronomer Robley Williams, knowing that the craters of the moon are best seen when oblique light on them results in shadows, proposed to the electron microscopist Ralph Wyckoff that they work out a technique for making viruses cast shadows on the background against which they were to be observed.

A spray of vaporized metal did the trick. It not only left a clear space behind each virus (as drifting snow sometimes does behind a fence post), but in addition it gave each virus a thin metallic coat which clearly defined its shape. And there they were: the big psittacosis viruses, the small polio viruses, and a host of others in between.

Incidentally, how big is "big" and how small is "small"? Fractions of inches are not precise enough for measuring miniaturized matter, so the standard measure in the little world we have now entered is the micron—approximately 1/25,000th of an inch. Objects of that size can *just* be seen with a fine optical microscope. The smaller objects made visible by the electron microscope are measured in *milli*microns—each of which is roughly 1/25,000,-000th of an inch.

In *Figure 74,* the circle represents a cell—call it a red blood cell—that, in an organism, is about eight microns (or eight thousand millimicrons) in diameter. Here, it has been magnified about 6250 times. The microorganisms inside it, in approximately correct relative sizes, are:

Figure 74

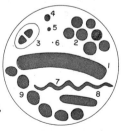

1. *The bacillus that causes anthrax,*
2. *The staphylococcus that causes boils,*
3. *The bacterium—a diplococcus— that causes pneumonia,*
4. *The psittacosis virus,*
5. *Vaccinia, the virus that causes cowpox,*
6. *The yellow fever virus,*
7. *The spirochete responsible for syphilis,*
8. *The colon bacillus which can cause infant diarrhea,*
9. *The streptococcus bacteria that cause scarlet fever.*

And where, in this lethal assembly, are the polio viruses, the influenza viruses, the tobacco mosaic viruses? We need still another degree of magnification to see them. *Figure 75* visualizes a cell that is only *one* micron in diameter, and the relatively large virus that you see inside it is one of the smaller ones in *Figure 74*. These are:

1. *Vaccinia,*
2. *The virus that causes polio,*
3. *Tobacco mosaic virus,*
4. *One of several viruses that attack colon bacilli,*
5. *The virus that causes influenza.*

Figure 75

These have all been magnified about 42,000 times. In life, the vaccinia are about 225 millimicrons in size, and the polio viruses are about 12 millimicrons in size.

We just said "in life. . . ." But *are* these tiny bodies alive? It was known from Stanley's work that they can make more of their kind. However, do they have genes that separate and recombine in accordance with the Mendelian laws that apply to other organisms? And what about bacteria? Do *they* mutate and pass on the altered characteristics that result from mutation? These questions absorbed many geneticists during the 1940's.

One of them were Joshua Lederberg, who began his work on bacterial genetics as a student of Tatum. Tatum had discovered some mutant strains of the colon bacillus. Like the Neurospora mutants, these were unable to synthesize some needed substance. And just as Morgan a generation before had used white-eyed fruit flies as genetic markers, so Lederberg used those mutant bacteria. He found that colon bacilli *do* have genes, carried in a single chromosome; and that a process akin to mating occurs, in which bacteria swap genes and thus turn out recombinations of themselves.

Cells of opposite mating types pair and form what is called a conjugation tube. The single chromosome of the donor cell moves slowly through the conjugation tube into the recipient cell, starting always at the same end (call it the head) and usually breaking before the process is completed. Some of its genes then recombine with genes from the cell it has entered. The complete donor chromosome rarely runs the entire course, and for this reason it is the genes at the front end of the migrating chromosome that are most likely to appear in the progeny of the new union.

Having learned this, and also that it takes a donor chromosome about an hour to travel through the conjugation tube, the French bacteriologists Jacob and Wollman interrupted the progress of millions of colon bacilli at various intervals during that hour. An early interruption of the process permits few donor genes to complete the journey; later interruptions allow more to pass through the tube. By checking the progeny resulting from each of these unions, they determined the linear order of genes in this particular kind of bacterium, and made chromosome maps for colon bacilli just as Sturtevant had done for fruit flies.

Bacteria and viruses infect other organisms to obtain nourishment for themselves and to produce more of their kind in a pleasant environment. However, if bacteria are put in a test tube full of the right nutrients, they do quite as well as if they were in a mouse, a man, or a lamb chop: they can make whatever they need for life. Not so with the viruses. They are parasites, and can reproduce only in living cells. They can't take raw materials from a test tube and transform them into the virus equivalent of blood and bone; they need to use the enzymes in living cells to run their own metabolic machinery. And their tastes (as you noted in connection with *Figures 74* and *75*) run the gamut from man to bacteria.

The viruses which attack the colon bacilli have been much studied. They are spherical, with tail-like projections by which each affixes itself to a bacillus—as ticks hang on a dog. (*Figure 76.*) The viruses puncture the

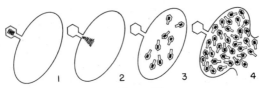

Figure 76

cell walls of their prey (1) and squirt their insides into it, leaving their "coats" outside (2) like emptied syringes. Inside the bacterium, the viruses multiply (3). Twenty minutes later, full to bursting with viruses that have used its contents for their own growth, the bacterium bursts (4). A hundred or more daughter viruses scatter into the nearby environment, each capable of creating another hundred like itself within another twenty minutes.[2] It's no wonder that such viruses are called bacteriophages ("bacteria eaters").

Thanks to the work of Alfred Hershey, Seymour Benzer, Max Delbrück, and other virologists, it is known that viruses have genes and undergo a kind of mating. If two virus particles differing from each other by two separate mutant genes simultaneously infect the same bacterial cell, not only do progeny like each of the parents appear, but also two recombination types as well. Furthermore, the rules of crossing-over as Morgan postulated them for fruit flies are just as applicable to viruses: genes that are close together in a linear series recombine with low frequency, genes that are far apart recombine with high frequency, and from recombination rates one can determine the position of each gene in the series.

It is one of the incredible accomplishments of modern science that genetic maps can be made for viruses—

2 This hundred-fold increase per twenty-minute generation means that a single virus particle could give rise to 100,000,000,000,000,-000,000,000,000,000,000,000,000,000,000,000,000,000,000,-000,000,000 progeny *within twelve hours*. Fortunately for other forms of life, there aren't that many host cells available. Besides, at this rate, the entire universe would be filled with viruses within twenty-four hours and they could scarcely get started on their journey.

maps which position specific subunits within particles which themselves are less than a millionth of an inch in size.

It is necessary now to add an amendment to this story of the "bacteria eaters." Sometimes they don't. A virus may invade a bacterium but, instead of multiplying, may simply attach itself to a bacterial chromosome and ride along from generation to generation. Occasionally, the virus brings with it a bit of genetic material from the bacterial cell in which it matured (much as people who live in furnished apartments take along a few personal belongings with each move); *and these carried-along genes may replace their counterparts in the chromosome of the new bacterial host*. This phenomenon is called "transduction."

Its occurrence at the virus-bacteria level of life makes scientists wonder if the viruses known to cause certain kinds of cancer in plants or animals do it by replacing genes in the cells they invade. Cancer is an uncontrolled growth of cells. Maybe a virus-engineered exchange of genes robbed those cells of their ability to control certain processes of cell growth.

And what about cancer in humans? Some people suspect that leukemia may be virus-induced, but this belief is not yet widely accepted. No viruses have been found in this or other kinds of human cancer, which medicine still classifies as neither infectious nor contagious. But it is reasonable to assume that what a virus can do in a plant or lower animal it can do in a human. The same principles govern the functioning of all living things.

Chapter 17

DNA OR PROTEIN?

Let us return now to the year 1869, three years after Mendel had published his monograph on peas. That's when a Swiss biochemist named Friedrich Miescher decided to try the enzyme pepsin as an agent for breaking down the protein in cells he wanted to study. It worked fine—except that a portion of each cell didn't disintegrate. That portion, he was surprised to find, was the nucleus. It had shrunk a bit, but otherwise seemed unchanged.

By the time Miescher had refined this nuclear residue to a white powder and had completed his chemical analysis of it, he had discovered that it was a phosphorus-containing substance quite unlike protein. It seemed logical, in view of its source, to call it "nuclein." He later discovered that salmon sperms (which are almost all nucleus) are particularly rich in this substance.

Study of it proceeded, though hardly at a breakneck pace; in the last part of the nineteenth century, the "hot" subject in biochemical circles was protein, and biologists were most interested in tracing the lineage of species whose evolution Darwin had so recently demonstrated. So it was forty years before the German Albrecht Kossel announced a further major fact about the stuff that meanwhile had been renamed "nucleic acid."

He found that it included four kinds of nitrogen-containing compounds, the type that chemists call "bases." The term is comparable to a family surname. However, just as various members of a family have individual names in addition to a joint surname, so the bases are divided into double-ring structures called purines and single-ring structures called pyrimidines. In this type of nucleic acid there are two kinds of purines: adenine and guanine; and two kinds of pyrimidines: thymine and cytosine.

Figure 77 shows the structural formulas of these substances (simplified by omitting hydrogen atoms, and repeated as undetailed silhouettes which you will soon find useful). Later it was found that there is another kind of nucleic acid. Its purines are just like the two shown above, and it also contains cytosine. But instead of thymine, its second pyrimidine is one called uracil (*Figure 78*). You'll note that these cousin molecules are almost the same; uracil lacks only the carbon atom that

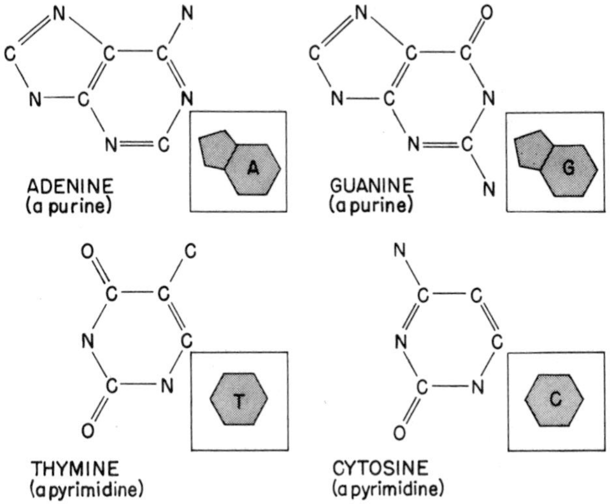

ADENINE
(a purine)

GUANINE
(a purine)

THYMINE
(a pyrimidine)

CYTOSINE
(a pyrimidine)

Figure 77

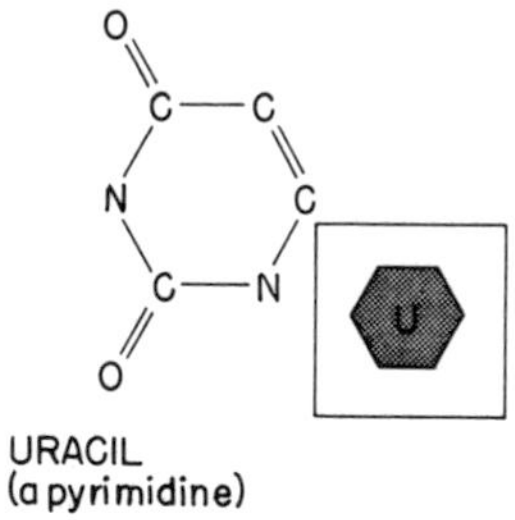

URACIL
(a pyrimidine)

Figure 78

appears in thymine in the position that airmen would call "two o'clock."

Both nucleic acids also contain sugar, but again with a difference. The one we have just described, the one that contains uracil instead of thymine, includes a molecule of *ribose* sugar, which (simplified) has a formula as diagrammed at left in *Figure 79*. The other kind of nucleic acid includes a molecule of *deoxyribose* sugar, a name which means that it has one less oxygen atom than ribose sugar. It is diagrammed at right in *Figure 79*. (The silhouettes take no account of atomic differences because they are not important to the use that will be made of the silhouettes.)

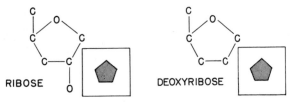

Figure 79

These sugars give the two kinds of nucleic acid their names. If a nucleic acid contains ribose sugar, it is called ribonucleic acid; if the deoxyribose sugar, deoxyribonucleic acid. In the twentieth-century fashion—who can give the full names of UNICEF, SEC, NASA, NATO, ASCAP, and all the rest?—both names are commonly abbreviated to the essential initials, and from here on you will hear only of RNA and DNA.

The final component of nucleic acid—either kind—is a phosphate group, one atom of phosphorus linked to four atoms of oxygen, as in *Figure 80*.

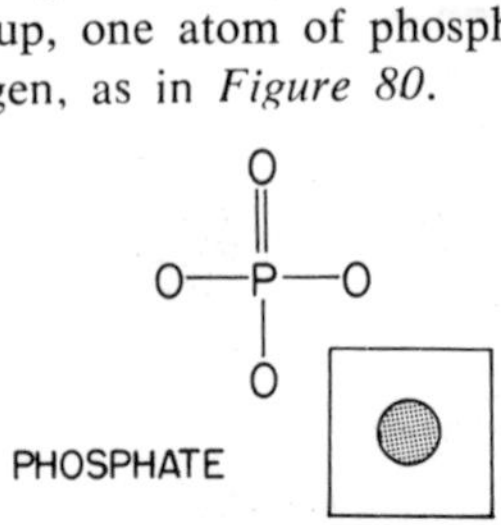

$$O=P$$

PHOSPHATE

Figure 80

These various components are hitched together into specific assemblies called nucleotides. Here, for example, is the "recipe" for DNA: Add to each base—adenine, guanine, cytosine, or thymine—one molecule of deoxyribose sugar and one phosphate group. Yield: four nucleotides. Whereas the recipe for RNA reads: Add to each base—adenine, guanine, cytosine, or *uracil*—one molecule of *ribose* sugar and one phosphate group. Yield: four nucleotides. In *Figure 81* we show, as an example, an adenine-containing nucleotide. The others are similarly structured.

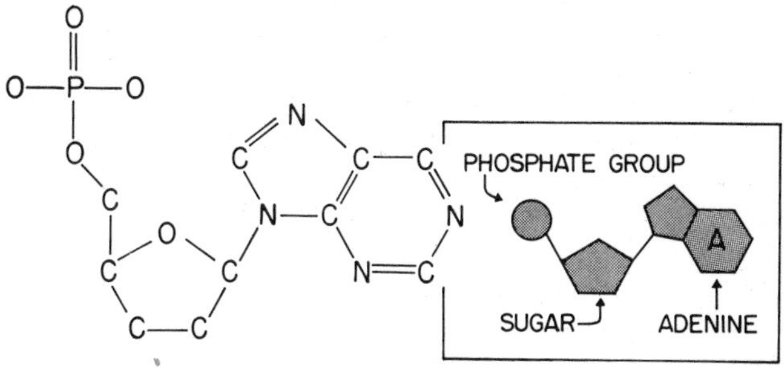

Figure 81

Nucleic acid research was long of more interest to chemists than to geneticists, except those of the latter who were interested in *any* information about the nucleus of the cell simply because it is the site of the chromosomes.

In the late 1920's such men engaged in lively speculation as to the significance of the German biochemist Robert Feulgen's discovery that the dye fuchsin combines with DNA but not with RNA, a staining technique which showed that the chromosomes are full of DNA, whereas the surrounding cell cytoplasm contains RNA.

In 1934, these finds were confirmed and amplified by the Swedish biochemist T. Caspersson, using a different research tool—photography of chromosomes under ultraviolet light. His photographs showed chromosomes as bodies striped with alternate light and dark bands, as if they were tubes full of lozenges with thin strips of protective material between them. Since DNA has a characteristic absorption rate of UV light (as it does of dye), the dark bands were thus indentified as agglomerations of DNA. This finding reinforced other evidence that genes are arranged in a linear series.[1]

Obviously then—if those bands are the genes, and the bands are DNA—the basic material of life must be DNA.

That's what one group of scientists said. Another group didn't believe that the conclusion was an obvious one at all. The chromosomes also contain protein. Maybe it's the protein, not the DNA, that carries the genetic instructions?

Thus began a decade of argument, bitter at times, which proved that scientists are as subjective as other men. An intuitive "feel" for how things ought to be is as useful in science as in cookery or in navigation, but that same intuition can play tricks on one, too—as when you're sure you are driving north and then discover you've gone miles due west. So it was with the proponents of protein as the carrier of genetic instructions. It just didn't seem *right* for DNA to be the dynamic component of the chromosomes.

The most convincing argument for identifying genes with protein rather than nucleic acid was the belief that DNA had a monotonous structure in which the nucleotides were arranged in repeating identical four-nucleotide segments. If this were so, nucleic acids could not have the specificity required of genes. On the other hand, it was known that there are a great many different kinds of proteins and that *their* specificity is determined by their amino acid sequences. So it is understandable that protein seemed to many to be more "alive" than the nucleic acid which most biologists knew only as a bottle of white powder on chemists' laboratory shelves.

During the 1940's, several investigators correlated DNA

---

[1] It was this work (on Drosophila salivary gland chromosomes, as mentioned in Chapter 13) that helped geneticists link specific positions on chromosomes with equivalent positions on genetic maps.

and protein distribution in the cells with the known processes of inheritance. It was learned that the amount of DNA in body cells varies from organism to organism— as does the number of chromosomes. It was learned that in any given organism the amount of DNA in body cells is twice the amount found in the sex cells—and this too is true of chromosome distribution. On the other hand, the amount of protein in various organisms and in specific cells is highly variable, and has no quantitative correlation with number or distribution of chromosomes. The pro-DNA side said: How could a substance so unevenly measured into the mix bring about the regular and predictable results characteristic of the hereditary units in chromosomes? The pro-protein side said: Even the smallest amount of protein *could* be enough.

What finally settled the controversy was the DNA of "dead" bacteria and of live viruses.

The bacteria were pneumococci, and their behavior in certain vaccines had been a mystery since 1928. In that year the English bacteriologist Fred Griffith was seeking better ways to control pneumonia, and injected a mouse with two standard vaccines—Type I, in which the germs are still alive but have lost their gelatinous coats and are therefore incapable of causing disease; and Type III, a heat-killed strain with intact coats. Neither vaccine should have made the mouse sick. But together they did. It got a mouse version of pneumonia—and a postmortem showed a heavy infection of live Type III pneumococcus bacteria (with intact coats).

One possible explanation, of course, was that the Type III bacteria in the injection hadn't really been killed. But inoculation of other mice from the same batch of vaccine produced no sickness. Then the only other explanation— and it was incredible—was that dead Type III bacteria had imposed their own hereditary character on the coatless but still living Type I's. It was like having a zombie in the lab. Furthermore, the change was permanent: when the new Type III's were injected into other mice, the mice became diseased and many Type III virulent bacteria could be recovered from them.

It wasn't until the 1940's that scientists had delicate enough investigative techniques available to them to get an answer to this puzzler. Then, at the Rockefeller Institute, O. T. Avery and his associates attacked it by step-by-step elimination procedures. First, they removed the gelatinous coat that encloses Type III pneumococci. *What was left in the cell could turn Type I bacteria into Type III.* Next, they leached out all the protein in that cell, leaving nothing but nucleic acid—DNA. *It could turn Type I bacteria into Type III.* Then the investigators reversed the procedure, removing the DNA from the cell and leaving only protein. When the protein from Type III cells was mixed with Type I cells, *nothing happened.* DNA, then, must be the basic material of life!

But perhaps the DNA of bacteria is unique?

In 1952, a virus and an elegant experiment provided the conclusive proof that a universal rule rather than an exception had been discovered.

You will remember that the viruses which prey on colon bacilli do so by affixing themselves to a bacterium and injecting their contents into the cell they are about to parasitize. There, they use the materials and the metabolic machinery in the bacterial cell to make replicas of themselves. Extrapolating from Avery's work, one might assume that it is the DNA in the viruses which directs the making of new viruses inside the bacterium.

The bacteriologists Alfred D. Hershey and Martha Chase found out that this is indeed the case by using the new radioactive isotopes[2] of phosphorus and sulfur that were a by-product of the wartime development of the atomic bomb. These emit electrons and can therefore be detected by a Geiger counter or by radio-sensitive photographic film.

Knowing that proteins contain sulfur but no phosphorus and that DNA contains phosphorus but no sulfur, Hershey and Chase grew a batch of colon bacilli on a

---

2 All elements have several versions with the same chemical properties but differing numbers of neutrons. These various versions are called "isotopes" of the given element.

culture which included radioactive sulfur. The bacteria, therefore, incorporated this sulfur into the proteins of their structure. Next, the bacteria were infected with the viruses that normally prey on them, and the viruses—in utilizing the contents of the bacterial cells for their own replication—incorporated the radioactive sulfur into *their* proteins.

Finally, these "labeled" viruses were introduced into a culture of ordinary colon bacilli. After the viruses had injected their contents into the bacteria, the infected bacteria were churned about in a Waring Blendor. The viral coats, adhering to the outer walls of each bacterium, were knocked off by the shearing forces of the blendor, and were later separated from the bacterial cells in a centrifuge. Then the radioactivity of the two sediments was checked. The viral coats contained the radioactive sulfur, proving that they were full of protein; but the bacterial cells were only slightly radioactive.

The same type of experiment was then carried out in reverse. Bacteria were grown on a medium incorporating radioactive phosphorus. This "label" was passed on to both the first and second generations of infecting viruses. When *their* coats were separated from the bacteria they had infected, the radioactivity was concentrated in the bacterial cells, very little appearing in the sheared-off coats—proving again that what went into the bacteria was DNA.

DNA, therefore, was established as the dynamic partner of the two major constituents of the virus. The protein coat seems to be protective only.[3]

But this knowledge threw no light on the big question of how DNA does what it does. Don't forget that only the DNA of viruses enters the bacteria, yet the new viruses that burst out of each infected bacterium are

---

[3] Yet, almost a decade after the Hershey-Chase experiment, Webster's Third New International Dictionary defines the gene as "one of the elements of the germ plasm serving as specific transmitters of hereditary characters and usually regarded as complex self-perpetuating protein molecules . . ."

complete with protein coats. Obviously, then, DNA transmits directions for the making of a complete organism.
What are the mechanisms? This was the problem facing
geneticists in the middle 1950's. Once again, a scientific
discovery had posed more questions than it answered.

Chapter 18

THE STRUCTURE OF DNA—THEORY

Just before the American chemist Linus Pauling went to
Sweden to accept the Nobel prize for his work on the
atomic structure of protein, his colleagues at Caltech
staged a lighthearted musical revue in his honor. A show-
stopper entitled "Crystal Crackin' Papa" (which was sung,
more or less, to the tune of "Pistol Packin' Mama")
included these words:

> Peptide bonds and side groups,
> He put them all in place;
> It sure was plain
> They formed a chain
> And had such helical grace . . .

"Helical" is the adjectival form of helix, which is a figure
in three-dimensional space patterned like the threads of a
screw or a spiral staircase. The interior of the Guggen-
heim Museum in New York City, its ramps rising as they
turn, is a helix.

What Pauling had shown, in 1950, was that a protein's
component chains of amino acids (which are called
peptides) are neatly arranged in the twisting turns of a
helix and are held in that configuration by hydrogen
bonds between successive turns of the helix. Research

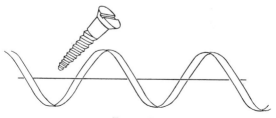

Figure 82

occurring at the same time, in various labs—notably by a group led by Maurice Wilkins of King's College, London —indicated that DNA molecules were likewise disposed in a helix. Scientists began to struggle in earnest with the *how* of DNA's structure.

Since the units that we are now talking about—atoms —are almost too small to comprehend, and are completely invisible, perhaps this is a good place to pause and look briefly at modern methods of investigation. How do scientists go about discovering the atomic structure of anything?

They begin with a chemical analysis. For example, it was found early in the nineteenth century that water can be decomposed electrolytically (between two oppositely charged plates) into hydrogen and oxygen, always in constant proportions of two-to-one. Later, when atomic weights could be assigned to the elements, it was discovered that this two-to-one relationship corresponded to two atoms of hydrogen to one atom of oxygen; and the chemical formula of water could be written as H_2O. Similarly, common table salt was found to consist of sodium and chlorine atoms in equal numbers ($NaCl$).

For complex molecules such as the amino acids or the nucleotides, more steps are involved. First one determines the kinds of atoms present, and their proportions. Then you go after the molecular subgroupings. In an amino acid, for example, the amino group (NH_2) has certain chemical properties, and so does the hydroxyl group (OH). Once the various subgroupings are identified, the chemical formula can be written. To a chemist, $CH_2(NH_2)COOH$ says "glycine" as clearly as the word itself.

As physicists have come to understand more about the nature of light and as technology has improved, it has become possible to analyze substances on the basis of how they respond to light. In the last chapter, for example, we mentioned Caspersson's photography of chromosomes under ultraviolet light. The bases within nucleotides absorb different wave lengths of visible, infrared, or ultraviolet light. The characteristic absorption patterns of these and other molecules, which can be measured with instruments called spectrophotometers, help determine a substance's chemical composition.

But what about its physical structure—the spatial arrangements of the atoms within a molecule? How does one find out how far apart the atoms are, or the angles and lengths of the chemical bonds that hold them together?

One powerful and widely used tool for getting answers to such questions is X-ray diffraction. In practice, this procedure is complex; but in principle it is simple. (*See Figure 83.*) A beam of light impinging on a flat mirror is reflected at an angle (R) exactly equal to the angle of incidence (I). You can check this yourself with a light source and a mirror. If one knows the position of the light source and the point of detection of the reflected light, the plane of the mirror can easily be determined—for the angles R and I must be equal, and only one position of the mirror will make them so.

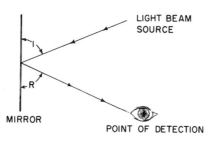

Figure 83

Now in crystals, say of salt (*shown in Figure 84*), the atoms are arranged in a regular pattern from which an incident beam of X-rays will be reflected as if the planes of atoms were mirrors. The X-rays register a pattern on a photographic plate that corresponds to the structural pattern of the crystal. It was by this X-ray diffraction technique that investigators "cracked" the structure of such simple crystals as those of salt and ice. Thus the positions of their atoms became known, and the distances between them.[1]

With considerable difficulty, the methods of X-ray diffraction have been extended to such complex organic molecules as the proteins and nucleic acids. But these

Figure 84

are giant molecules with a great many subgroupings, and X-rays bounce off so many planes that it is sometimes difficult to read the photographic record. This is the point at which model-building becomes useful.

Pauling and his collaborator Robert Corey worked out the so-called alpha helix configuration of protein molecules in this way. (At Caltech, their models were called their "Tinker Toys.") Once a model is constructed that is consistent with available information on interatomic distances, bond angles, X-ray diffraction patterns, and so on, predictions can be made regarding additional X-ray diffraction patterns that should exist. If these are then confirmed, the evidence of the correctness of the structure is greatly strengthened.

In the same year that the structure of protein was discovered—1950—the University of Indiana awarded a

---

1 Incidentally, when science began to probe the atom, a new micromeasure was needed. You will remember that things the size of viruses are measures in millimicrons, which are roughly 1/25,000-000th of an inch. Atoms, of course, are much smaller than viruses; hence, atomic measurements are expressed in Ångstrom units, after the Swedish astronomer who suggested them. An Ångstrom ("Å") unit is 1/10th of a millimicron in size; that is, 1/250,000,000th of an inch.

Ph.D. degree to a rugged individualist named James Dewey Watson. His doctoral research had centered on details of radiation effects on bacterial viruses; to pursue it further, he was awarded a fellowship by the National Research Council and went to the University of Copenhagen.

A year later he informed the fellowship committee that he had changed horses. He'd decided, he told them, that the most important problem in genetics was to determine the structure of DNA; therefore, that's what he wanted to work on. To do so he went to Cambridge University to collaborate with the British chemist Francis Crick.

The committee was not enthusiastic. There was the matter of setting a precedent for midstream changes. There was Watson's own capability to consider. He was not yet twenty-five years old; how likely was it that he could solve a problem that was stumping older and wiser men? Permission was therefore at first refused.

Watson stubbornly said he was going to work at Cambridge anyway, and he did. Although the fellowship committee later invited him to reapply for a portion of his original grant, he had meanwhile obtained support from the National Foundation for Infantile Paralysis. When the Watson-Crick collaboration produced a theory that many scientists consider the most momentous since Mendel's, the original committee, one suspects, may have experienced anguish somewhat akin to that of a bettor who has thrown away his ticket on the long-shot winner of a Kentucky Derby.

What the American biochemist and the English chemist did was to fit the known chemical facts about DNA into a proposed molecular structure that explains how DNA makes copies of itself. In so doing, they also enabled science to discover how genetic directions are "written," how they are translated into orders which the cells obey, and how they are modified by mutation. Finally, they enabled chemists, physicists, and biologists to discuss the structure and behavior of living organisms—for the first time in the history of science—in a common language, the language of molecular structure.

Watson and Crick did no research—as laymen understand the word. They reread all the literature about DNA; they covered paper and blackboards with formulas and equations; they snipped "nucleotides" from thin metal sheets and used them for model-making. But mostly they just *thought*.

Their object was to put together the following pieces of an atomic jigsaw puzzle:

1. It was known from X-ray diffraction studies that the bases, sugars, and phosphates in each nucleotide are joined in the pattern shown in *Figure 85* in a strand at least 200,000 such units long per molecule.

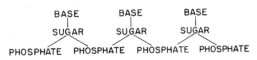

Figure 85

2. In addition to the dots and splashes spaced to correspond to the phosphate-sugar-base relationship shown above, the X-ray plates also showed another wider-spaced set of markings that almost certainly reflected the turns of a helix. The diameter of this helix was known: it is of uniform width, about 20 Å across.

3. Whether the sugars and phosphates are on the "outside" and the bases closer to the axis of the helix, or vice versa, was not known. Nor was it known whether all three components of a nucleotide are oriented alike, as at left in *Figure 86* (using drinking glasses as an example)

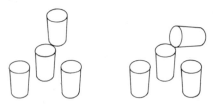

Figure 86

or whether the bases are turned at right angles to the sugars and phosphates, as at right in *Figure 86*. There was some evidence indicating the right-angled orientation, so Watson and Crick provisionally opted for that belief.

4. Quantitative analysis by various chemists had shown that in all organisms the sugars and phosphates are in the same proportion, thus confirming the regularity of sequence shown by X-ray diffraction studies.

5. But different organisms vary greatly in total amounts of adenine, guanine, cytosine, and thymine. One organism can have twice as many thymine-containing nucleotides as another organism, for example. This could only mean that there is no particular regularity of sequence governing the order of bases.

6. Offsetting this apparent complete variability was a curious fact that had been turned up by the American biochemist Erwin Chargaff. Within the DNA of any particular organism, the ratio of nucleotides containing adenine to those containing thymine is one-to-one, and so is that of nucleotides containing guanine to those containing cytosine.

In other words, your cells and the cells of a rabbit may have different total amounts of the four bases, but in both you and the rabbit the amount of adenine equals the amount of thymine, and the guanine equals the cytosine.

This latter point was really the key to the structure that Watson and Crick finally proposed, because it suggested, first, that adenine and thymine are paired and so are guanine and cytosine; and, second, that a pairing of bases within nucleotides requires the DNA strands of which they are a part to be paired, too. In other words, the DNA helix must be a *double* strand.

A chemical condition would have to be met, however, before one could postulate such pairing. The bases in the two strands would have to come together in such a way that hydrogen bonds would form. Assuming that the bases are right-angled relative to the sugars and phosphates, such bonds will form only at points indicated in the formulas in *Figure 87*.

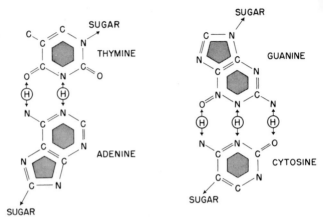

Figure 87

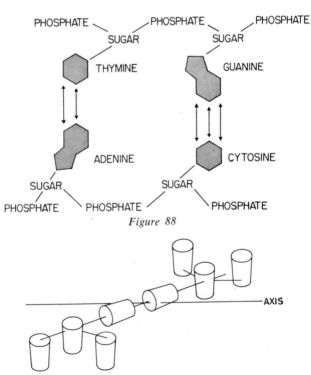

Figure 88

Figure 89

If the bases are bonded in this fashion, the sugars and phosphates become positioned on the outside of each strand of DNA as shown in *Figure 88*.

In three dimensions, the assembly would appear as in *Figure 89*.

And flattened out into a diagrammatic representation, it would look like *Figure 90*.

Such an assembly, except for one fact, could be written thus:

Adenine Cytosine Thymine Adenine Cytosine Thymine
   | | | | | |
Thymine Guanine Adenine Thymine Guanine Adenine

That one fact is apparent if you study the bases in the top strand—take an adenine, for example—and compare it with the same base in the bottom strand. You'll soon realize that each is a reversal of the other.

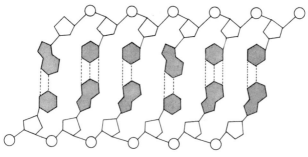

Figure 90

Watson and Crick knew what this reversal means: the nucleotides and therefore the two strands of the helix are "anti-parallel"—that is, positioned relative to each other (to resurrect a figure of speech used earlier in this book) like two swimmers headed in opposite directions, one face-down and doing the crawl, the other face-up and doing the backstroke. Therefore, the accurate way to write a series of pairings as above is:

ǝuıuǝp∀ ǝuısoʇʎƆ ǝuıɯʎɥʇ ǝuıuǝp∀ ǝuısoʇʎƆ ǝuıɯʎɥʇ
   | | | | | |
Thymine Guanine Adenine Thymine Guanine Adenine

And a good way to identify the bases on a diagram is:

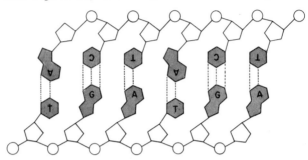

Figure 91

Now, by turning *Figure 91* into a helix, one gets *Figure 92*. The sugars and phosphates on the outside of each strand would be held in steady alignment because the paired bases would serve as "connecting rods." A fact that fitted here was that X-ray diffraction studies showed the DNA molecule to be of uniform diameter. The pairing of a double-ring with a single-ring base in each case would add up to the same over-all width for each pair.

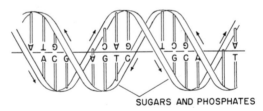

SUGARS AND PHOSPHATES

Figure 92

In sum, everything about this possible structure corresponded to what was known about the physical nature of DNA. But the most exciting aspect of Watson and Crick's emerging solution for their atomic jigsaw puzzle was that molecules of this design could make copies of themselves —which DNA was, of course, known to do.

If the hydrogen bonds between the two strands were to break (*see Figure 93*), the two strands were to unwind,

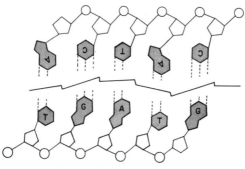

Figure 93

and the bases in each strand were to pick up (from raw materials in the cell) their proper partners (*see Figure 94*), each double-stranded DNA molecule would have made a copy of itself!

It must have required almost superhuman restraint for Watson and Crick to write in their published account, "It has not escaped our notice that the specific pairing we have postulated immediately suggests a possible copying mechanism for the genetic material."

The two men also realized that so long as A in one chain paired with T in the other chain, and C in one chain with G in the other, the over-all sequence could be infinitely varied.

If *any* sequence of the four pairs—A-T, T-A, C-G, and G-C—is possible (and chemists' quantitative analysis, remember, had found widely differing amounts of the bases in different organisms), the possible variations are astronomical. Just four pairs seem a small and limiting number only up to the point where you envision them strung in chains of approximately 200,000, the number of nucleotides estimated to be contained in some DNA molecules. Yes, such a structure would well explain the endless diversity among living things.

It was a wonderfully neat theory. In fact, it was almost *too* neat.

Watson and Crick had talked to Maurice Wilkins at King's College. He and his colleagues had made much

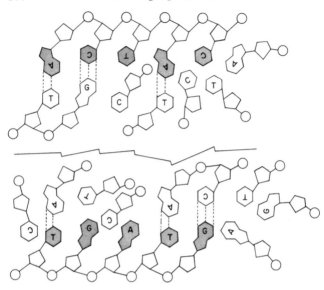

Figure 94

progress in studying DNA by X-ray diffraction techniques, and the scientific grapevine was buzzing with news about what they were finding. It confirmed what Watson and Crick had deduced (and vice versa): that the DNA molecule is a double helix, anti-parallel in structure, the sugar-phosphates on the outside being linked by the bases.

Therefore, in 1953, publication was joint—Watson and Crick emphasizing the specific pairing of nucleotides that was their unique contribution, Wilkins emphasizing the structural details as revealed by X-ray diffraction. The complementarity of the data provided by the two sets of investigators strengthened their case.

Nevertheless, a sizable number of scientists couldn't accept it. Some objected for a wholly subjective and non-scientific reason: the great mystery of life couldn't, at its base, be that simple. Others criticized details. How could a chain of 200,000 or more nucleotides unwind and rewind within minutes? By what stretch of the imagination could one assume that 200,000 additional nucleotides of exactly the right kind would be floating around in the cell at just the right moment? Let alone the several *billion* that would be needed when a human cell, its forty-six chromosomes each containing far more than 200,000 nucleotides per chromosome, replicated. Finally, what possible device could the cell possess for getting the correct partners together? To do all these things, they said, would require a degree of precision, speed, and coordination that was inconceivable. And in this assessment they were quite right: the cellular processes that are triggered by DNA *are* almost inconceivably precise, swift, and well-coordinated. But the inconceivable is not necessarily impossible, nor was it in this case.

Chapter 19

THE STRUCTURE OF DNA—PROOF

Proof that the Watson-Crick structure was essentially correct came fast; and when it came, it was almost as elegant as the initial hypothesis.

One part of the proof resulted from the use of an analytical ultracentrifuge. In a proper solution and when spun with extreme rapidity, molecules of varying densities suspend themselves at different levels in the liquid—a kind of invisible layering, but one which can be read by chemists as successfully as geologists read the visible evidence of rock layers in a gorge. The position of a given band indicates the density of the molecules that compose it; and if the molecules in that band are DNA you can check how much DNA is present by exposing it to ultraviolet light and measuring the amount of UV absorption.

Knowing this, Matthew Meselson, Frank Stahl, and Jerome Vinograd (all then at Caltech) grew several generations of colon bacilli on a culture medium containing N^{15}, a heavy stable isotope of nitrogen—a procedure which increases the molecular weight and density of the DNA in those bacteria by about 1 per cent over those that contain only the normal N^{14} isotope. DNA from bacteria nurtured on these two different culture mediums will "band" in an ultracentrifuge at two different levels, as in *Figure 95*.

Having bred bacteria with built-in "heavy" DNA, the three chemists then grew a generation on a culture medium containing only the "light"—N^{14}—nitrogen. Their reasoning was as follows: If the Watson-Crick hypothesis is correct, and the two chains of DNA *do* make complete duplicates of themselves, the first generation of bacteria (as determined by a doubling of the number of cells) should have one heavy and one light chain in each DNA molecule (*see Figure 96*). And those

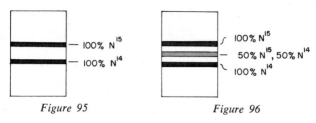

Figure 95   Figure 96

molecules should form a band in the ultracentrifuge exactly intermediate in density between N^{15} heavy and N^{14} light DNA. Which is exactly what happened when the experiment was done.

Then Meselson and his colleagues grew a second generation (determining two generations when each original cell had increased to four), again on a medium containing light nitrogen. This time, according to theory, half the DNA molecules should be composed of one chain containing N^{15} and one chain containing N^{14}, whereas the other half of DNA molecules should have N^{14} in both chains. DNA in the centrifuge should band equally in two positions, light and intermediate (*see Figure 97*). Which is also what happened.

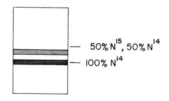

Figure 97

Another version of the same approach was the labeling of DNA in bean plant chromosomes with tritium (radioactive hydrogen-3) by the American cytologist J. Herbert Taylor and his associates.

If you dope broad bean root cells with colchicine (it's a gout remedy for humans, too), cell division will cease but the chromosomes inside those cells will continue to replicate. Taylor therefore fed the bean cells thymine which had been exposed to tritium. This put a radioactive

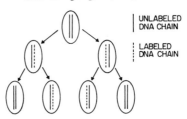

UNLABELED
DNA CHAIN

LABELED
DNA CHAIN

Figure 98

raw material, whose presence could later be detected on film, into the environment in which the chromosomes would be duplicating. Then an application of colchicine stopped cell division. This enabled investigators, after counting the number of chromosomes in a given cell, to determine how many chromosome replications had occurred within a given period.

If the Watson-Crick theory was right, as the strands of DNA separated for the first chromosome replication and each strand picked up a new partner strand, the thymine-containing nucleotides in the new molecule would be radioactive. Therefore all chromosomes of that "generation" would contain one labeled and one unlabeled strand as in *Figure 98*. On the *next* replication—the cell nutrients in this case being unlabeled—one would expect (again if the Watson-Crick theory is correct) to find that half the daughter chromosomes are radioactive and the other half are not.

And that too is what happened when the experiment was made.[1] The tritium-labeling of DNA in whole chromosomes gave a result which agreed with the nitrogen labeling experiments of Meselson.

---

[1] It should be mentioned that chromosomes do not contain just one longitudinal double DNA molecule the same length as the chromosome. In fact, DNA is coiled into the chromosomes so compactly that it may be a thousand times longer than the chromosome. But the point of Taylor's experiment was that the chromosome segments behaved *as if* each contained only one double molecule of DNA. Clearly the individual molecules of DNA replicated with each chromosome duplication in a manner consistent with the Watson-Crick hypothesis.

Still more evidence that the Watson-Crick hypothesis is correct came from the synthesis of DNA, in 1956, by Arthur Kornberg (then at Washington University, St. Louis). This achievement caused newspapers to break out in a rash of headlines predicting that living things will be created in a test tube any day now. Happily or alas, according to one's point of view, the brave new world is not yet at hand; nevertheless, Kornberg's achievement was a great one. He proved that the nucleotide bases in DNA *do* replicate by finding their complements.

It is necessary to interrupt at this point to remind you that all chemical reactions in a cell are engineered by enzymes. DNA is like a plant manager. Enzymes are its section foremen. The cytoplasm of the cell is a stock room full of necessary raw materials, including the high-energy phosphates which supply the "push" required to join groups of atoms into molecules. Whenever DNA says the word, the enzymes see to it that whatever materials have to be collected *are* collected and whatever energy has to be supplied *is* supplied.

Returning to Kornberg's experiment: First, he mixed together in a test tube the raw materials that DNA would need to duplicate itself: the four nucleotides (with two extra phosphate groups on each), inorganic salts, magnesium, and an enzyme required for DNA construction. Then he popped in a bit of natural DNA from a colon bacillus. Using the materials in its artificial environment, it made copies of itself. Furthermore, these copies made copies of *themselves*.

Some time later, an even more astounding event occurred.

We have not said much, so far, about the necessity of establishing "controls"—but when doing an experiment one must always try a variety of methods in order to check the nature and authenticity of a reaction. With regard to Kornberg's experiment just described, for example, one would assume that all four nucleotides must be present in the vessel in order for DNA synthesis to take place; but the only way to *know* whether this is the case is to set up a battery of test tubes, omit one or more nucleotides from each, and observe what happens. This is what Kornberg and his associates did. They discovered that the logical assumption *is* correct: for a bit of natural DNA to copy itself in an artificial environment such as they had created, all four nucleotides are necessary.

In doing this experiment, Kornberg had incubated his mixes for two to three hours, then had used optical and chemical methods for measuring the increase in DNA. In 1957, however, he and his colleagues decided to try a new measurement technique. Would the increase in DNA correlate with an increase in the viscosity of the solution in which the DNA was replicating? Again, they set up the same controls that had been used previously; but this time, in addition, they took measurements for longer than the two to three hours that had been the cut-off point before.

The investigators were happy to discover that viscosity *did* correlate with increase in DNA. They had indeed found a useful new method of measurement. But they found something else, too—something much more important. In one of the control test tubes, a solution from which guanine nucleotide had been omitted—and in which, therefore, no natural DNA could have been synthesized—an investigator noted, at the fourth hour, that a very rapid increase in viscosity was taking place. This continued until the sixth hour. If increase in viscosity correlated with the formation of DNA, DNA must have formed in that test tube—but how could it have, without one of the nucleotides?

That evening, Kornberg and his associates considered their several possible sources of error. Perhaps someone had mistakenly put into the mix the guanine that should have been omitted. Perhaps the control test tube had been contaminated by bacteria. Perhaps there was something wrong with the equipment that measured viscosity. Therefore, they reran the experiment the next day, being sure to eliminate each possible source of error. The same rapid increase in viscosity, at the same time interval after incubation, again occurred.

Controls were again set up, each omitting various of

the ingredients known to be essential for laboratory synthesis of DNA. It was found that, given enough time, rapid increase in viscosity occurred even in the test tube from which natural DNA—the model, or "primer," in previous experiments—had been omitted. This particular vessel produced an unusual kind of DNA, with the following sequence:

$$ \text{V} \perp \text{V} \perp \text{V} \perp \text{V} \perp \text{V} \perp $$
$$ \cdot \ \cdot \ \cdot \ \cdot \ \cdot \ \cdot \ \cdot \ \cdot \ \cdot $$
$$ \text{T A T A T A T A T A} $$

Subsequently, another experimental mix produced another unusual DNA. It had this sequence:

$$ \text{C} \ \text{Ɔ} \ \text{Ɔ} \ \text{C} \ \text{Ɔ} \ \text{Ɔ} \ \text{C} \ \text{Ɔ} \ \text{C} $$
$$ \cdot \ \cdot \ \cdot \ \cdot \ \cdot \ \cdot \ \cdot \ \cdot \ \cdot $$
$$ \text{G G G G G G G G G} $$

Both types, once made, produced copies of themselves— and without the four-to-six-hour lag period.

Note that Kornberg's original intention was not to find out whether DNA synthesis would take place without a bit of natural DNA as the model; he and his colleagues were simply running a routine check on the raw-material requirements of natural DNA when replicating in an artificial environment. What they found is a scientific example of serendipity.

Here, then, at a more advanced level of life, was reinforcement for the findings of experiments that had recreated a supposed primeval atmosphere and had made in it organic molecules from non-organic raw materials. Stanley Miller, in 1952, had gone back four or five billion years in his laboratory; Kornberg, in 1957, perhaps three billion.

It is amusing to note that when Kornberg undertook these experiments he was repeatedly warned by friends and colleagues that he didn't have a chance of success, and why go knowingly into a dead-end street? But he decided to risk a big failure, knowing that the opposite side of the same coin was a big success—and he proved that the process of replication isn't as complex as most people imagined.

In so doing, he did something even more important: he knocked the final prop from under the comfortable assumption of mankind that "life" is inherently different from "non-life."

Chapter 20

THE RNA BRIDGE BETWEEN DNA
AND PROTEIN

The postulation of the Watson-Crick structure for DNA was followed by such an explosion of research into the nature and function of the nucleic acids that it is almost impossible to tell the story from now on as a historical chronology, or to credit each investigator who has contributed significantly to the new knowledge. Perhaps the best indication of how swiftly science has stripped the cell of its secrets lies in this fact: of twenty-four persons awarded Nobel prizes in chemistry or the joint category medicine-physiology during the eight-year period 1958–65, fourteen worked directly on genetics, proteins, or nucleic acids.

They started with a redefinition of the gene: it is a segment of a DNA molecule. They reviewed what they knew of its role in life: first, to copy itself and thus to pass on to other generations the directions it contains; second, to control the chemical reactions in the cells of which it is a part, and thus to control the growth and function of the entire organism.

The second activity is the one that will concern us now.

It was known in the 1940's that DNA directs the making of the proteins that are one of the most important single substances in the body. But how? Some researchers attacked the question from the protein end, others from the DNA end; and they all found themselves meeting on a bridge of RNA.

RNA, as you will recall, is the *other* nucleic acid, the one that contains uracil (instead of thymine) and ribose sugar, the kind that is richer in oxygen than the deoxyribose sugar that gives DNA its name. The molecular structure of RNA is like that of its relative, except that it often takes the form of a single strand instead of a matched pair. (DNA does, too; but so rarely that we won't go into the details.) Sometimes RNA is the only nucleic acid present in an organism, and it then—even with one strand instead of two—acts as the primary director of life processes, just as DNA does.[1]

But all organisms that are multicellular contain *both* DNA and RNA, and it seemed unlikely that they would duplicate each other's activity. Therefore, many research efforts of the 1940's and 1950's concentrated on determining the specific role of each. It soon became clear that although DNA may carry the blueprint for proteins, it is RNA that does the work of making them. The following facts support this statement:

1. Tissues and organs that make large amounts of protein are richer in RNA than those which do not. Liver cells, for example, contain much more RNA than brain cells.

2. Within any given cell, DNA is found mostly in the nucleus, RNA in the cytoplasm.

3. The cytoplasm contains two kinds of RNA: one kind appears as relatively small molecules, free-floating; the other, as larger molecules associated with particles called "ribosomes."[2]

4. Studies by several investigative groups indicated that ribosomes are where protein is made.

Everything, in short, pointed to RNA as the agent that transmits DNA's instructions to the ribosomes.

The evidence strongly suggests that DNA makes a chain of the large-molecule RNA by the same template mechanism it uses to reproduce itself, in the course of which the DNA sequence of nucleotides is changed to a sequence characteristic of RNA. This new chain then

[1] RNA is the only nucleic acid present in that much-studied organism, tobacco mosaic virus. In 1955, at the University of California, Heinz Fraenkel-Conrat completely separated the RNA and protein components of TMV, dumped the much-processed residues back into a test tube, and had the astounding experience of seeing them become viable viruses again. RNA directed the reassembly.

[2] There is a third type of RNA that is a structural part of ribosomes. We shall not further speak of this.

makes its way from the nucleus of the cell to the ribosomes in the cytoplasm. There is a fine descriptive name for such a molecule: "messenger RNA."

(We're about to give an example of this process, but for your easier comprehension we are abandoning the convention of using upside-down letters to indicate the nucleotides in one strand of each complementary chain. Whenever, in the following pages, you see a double strand, try to visualize it as assembled in the correct anti-parallel fashion.)

Suppose now that a certain segment of DNA directs the formation of a particular kind of hemoglobin, and that that segment includes this sequence of bases:

GTGCAAAATAATTGGGGGCTTCTTTTT

If it were to *duplicate* itself, each base would find its complement—thymine pairing with adenine, guanine with cytosine, so:

GTGCAAAATAATTGGGGGCTTCTTTTT
. . . . } DNA
CACGTTTTATTAACCCCCGAAGAAAAA

After which, the two chains would wind around each other in a double helix, and you'd have another chain of DNA—another copy of the recipe for making hemoglobin.

But you wouldn't have any hemoglobin.

"Messenger RNA" could take care of that job—but only if adenine, which pairs with thymine in DNA replication, has equal affinity for uracil when the object is to make RNA. So:

GTGCAAAATAATTGGGGGCTTCTTTTT ←DNA
. . . .
CACGUUUUAUUAACCCCCGAAGAAAAA ←RNA
↑ ↑ ↑ ↑   ↑ ↑

In addition, a different sugar molecule would have to be incorporated in the backbone of the new nucleotide chain. Finished, the chain of RNA would detach itself from the DNA matrix, ease out of the nucleus of the

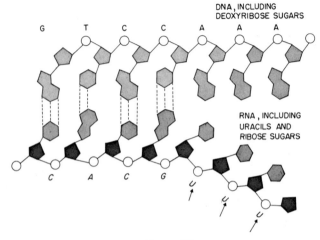

Figure 99

cell, and head for the ribosomes—in the manner depicted in *Figure 99*.

This is a fine theory, but is there any proof for it? Yes.

You will remember that when colon bacilli are attacked by a particular kind of virus, the protein coat of the virus is left outside the bacterium, viral DNA enters the cell and modifies the metabolic machinery of the bacterium in its own behalf. The bacterium ends up making viruses, complete with protein coats.

If the messenger RNA theory is correct, the RNA responsible for making those new protein coats ought to contain C-G and U-A in proportions equal to the proportions of C-G and T-A in the virus's DNA—which would prove that one was made on a template supplied by the other. Or so reasoned Elliot Volkin and Lazarus Astrachan of Oak Ridge National Laboratory. And that's how their experiment showed it to be. One of the RNA types in infected colon bacilli reflected the base composition of virus DNA and not the bacteria's own DNA.

Additional proof came from labeling plants or animals with radioactive isotopes. A representative example was Marko Zalokar's "tagging" of uracil with tritium (radioactive hydrogen) and then adding it to the culture medium in which bread mold was growing. After the plants had taken up uracil, he examined their cells at intervals of a few minutes. He discovered that as he began his examinations, the *nucleus* of each cell was radioactive, but eight minutes later the radioactivity was concentrated in the *ribosomes*. Since only RNA contains uracil, here was additional evidence that messenger RNA is made in the nucleus and then moves to the ribosomes.

Finally, groups at three different universities[3] made test tube solutions which included the essential chemicals in cell cytoplasm, added a bit of DNA, and then put in the enzyme known to be the catalyst necessary to RNA formation. It did a good job: the reaction that resulted was the construction of a chain of RNA complementary to the DNA "sample."

O.K. Knowing that DNA can transcribe into messenger RNA a sequence of instructions telling the cell how to make a certain protein, the next question was: How are amino acids (the building blocks of protein) ordered into the sequence that messenger RNA specifies?

The template idea had been a good one, so far; maybe the amino acids are positioned against the messenger RNA chain. But if so, what's the relationship? One amino acid to each base, or one amino acid to *several* bases?

A little arithmetic indicates the answer.

If you suppose a 1:1 relationship, you'd end up with no more than four amino acids, those attached to each

A U C G

and there are twenty amino acids. So a 1:1 relationship is out.

Well, then, what if the relationship of base to amino acid were 2:1? Here are the possible combinations:

AA AC AG AU GA GG GC GU CA CG CC CU UA UG UC UU

---

3 Samuel Weiss at the University of Chicago, Jerard Hurwitz at New York University, and Audrey Stevens at St. Louis University, and collaborators.

There are still not enough. A template of RNA based on only sixteen combinations couldn't easily specify all twenty amino acids.

Therefore, the answer almost has to be that groups of at least *three* bases equal *one* amino acid. Or, to be more precise, the 64-"word" vocabulary below allows the making of twenty amino acids even if some should be specified by two bases and others by three bases; and there are "words" left over which might carry other instructions pertaining to protein synthesis (such as "start" and "stop").

AAU	AGU	ACU	AUU	GAU	GGU	GCU	GUU
AAC	AGC	ACC	AUC	GAC	GGC	GCC	GUC
AAG	AGG	ACG	AUG	GAG	GGG	GCG	GUG
AAA	AGA	ACA	AUA	GAA	GGA	GCA	GUA
CAU	CGU	CCU	CUU	UAU	UGU	UCU	UUU
CAC	CGC	CCC	CUC	UAC	UGC	UCC	UUC
CAG	CGG	CCG	CUG	UAG	UGG	UCG	UUG
CAA	CGA	CCA	CUA	UAA	UGA	UCA	UUA

We'll give detailed consideration to this "triplet code" in the next chapter, but first let's pursue the question of how any three bases on an RNA chain could attract to themselves just the right amino acid out of twenty kinds floating around in the cell cytoplasm.

Hemoglobin molecules, for instance, contain two kinds of protein chains, alpha and beta, each in duplicate. The alpha chain is made up of 141 amino acids; the beta chain, of 146. That means that each of the two kinds of messenger RNA templates must be 423 and 438 bases long. And it *is* hard to visualize a process of selection so discriminating that a chain of about 440 bases could pull to itself over 140 amino acids within a minute (the length of time it takes each chain in hemoglobin to form) after beginning the process of assembly.

It would greatly speed such assembly, Francis Crick suggested, if there were another kind of RNA, a unit more mobile than messenger RNA. What if each three-base "word" in messenger RNA had a partner molecule which cruises around in the cell until it happens upon

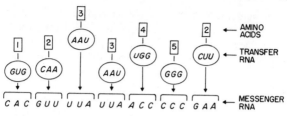

Figure 100

one specific amino acid, which it then transfers to the proper spot on the main RNA template? If such a molecule—it has since come to be called "transfer RNA"—were complementary to the triplet bases in the messenger RNA, and also had some kind of an atomic hook that would enable it to haul its proper amino acid to the RNA template, the assembly process would proceed as shown in *Figure 100*.

The science writer Ruth Moore[4] uses the analogy of tugs towing barges to describe the action of transfer RNA. It's an apt figure of speech. The final act after "dockage" of the transfer RNA tugs would be for the amino acids to chain together in the sequence

1-2-3-3-4-5-2

thus becoming the manufactured version of the protein blueprint in the messenger RNA template.

And this theory, too, is fundamentally correct. In one of the happiest coincidences of science, Crick proposed it just as Mahlon Hoagland and his associates at Harvard (who were interested in finding out how proteins are made rather than in molecular structure per se) discovered that amino acids hook to RNA before they link to each other in protein. And to what RNA do they hook? To the small molecules of RNA that electron microscopists had earlier discovered floating free in the cytoplasm outside the ribosomes!

Evidence from a great many laboratories now tells us that there is a separate transfer RNA molecule for each

[4] In *The Coil of Life* (New York: Alfred A. Knopf, 1961).

amino acid; that it is a double-stranded helix which is about 77 nucleotides long; and that it possesses suitable atomic "hooks" for attaching to an amino acid. The hook is the presence on all transfer RNA of the sequence ACC at the end of the helix where the amino acids attach. At the other end, transfer RNA attaches to the messenger RNA template via a three-base group complementary to a triplet on the template. The net effect, as shown in *Figure 101*, is that amino acids get positioned in a particular sequence relative to the sequence of

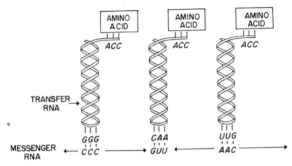

Figure 101

nucleotide bases in messenger RNA. And that's how proteins are formed in accordance with the directions carried in the master molecule, DNA.

Perhaps it has occurred to you that it might be the amino acid which somehow "recognizes" the section of the template with which it should be aligned, and that it takes the initiative in making the linkages which eventually produce protein?

This possibility was disproved in a brilliant experiment by a group of workers from the Rockefeller Institute, Johns Hopkins, and Purdue. They knew that the amino acid cysteine is transported to the messenger RNA template by one kind of transfer RNA, and that the amino acid alanine is transported by another kind of transfer RNA. The two amino acids differ only in that cysteine has a sulfur atom and alanine has none. So the investigators labeled cysteine with radioactive carbon, and after it had attached itself to its proper bit of RNA they exposed this molecular sub-assembly to a nickel catalyst. The catalytic treatment didn't break up the amino acid-transfer RNA linkage, but it *did* remove the sulfur—thereby turning cysteine into alanine. The action of transfer RNA was unaffected: it towed its brand-new alanine cargo to the proper location for cysteine, proving that it's the RNA that does the "recognizing," not the amino acids.

As a result of knowledge gained from these and many other studies, one might liken the processes by which DNA makes protein to an evenly paced and magnificently synchronized relay race. Here, for instance, is a summary of how you acquired one of the four protein chains in a hemoglobin molecule:

In the nucleus of one potential blood cell, a double helix of DNA partially unwound, its paired nucleotides parting as if they were the meshed teeth of a zipper.

RNA nucleotides, having been dispensed from a storehouse called the nucleolus, then attached to their complements in one of the free strands of the master molecule as it uncoiled.

Next, this strand of messenger RNA detached itself from the DNA template on which it had modeled itself, moved through the membrane surrounding the nucleus of the cell, and into the cytoplasm.[5]

ᵡ Cytoplasm is characteristically stocked with a rich assortment of enzymes, amino acids, and transfer RNA molecules. There, too, are the mitochondria, the power plants where high-energy phosphates are manufactured; and the spherical ribosomes. It was with these latter that the ribbon of RNA then associated itself.

---

[5] In most body cells, after unwinding to allow the formation of messenger RNA, DNA rewinds—thus preserving, in the nucleus, the prototype molecule. But circulating red blood cells in mammals are atypical; their nuclei break down in the course of hemoglobin formation. The cells make hemoglobin for a relatively short time, then disintegrate, thus requiring much more frequent replacement than is characteristic of other kinds of cells.

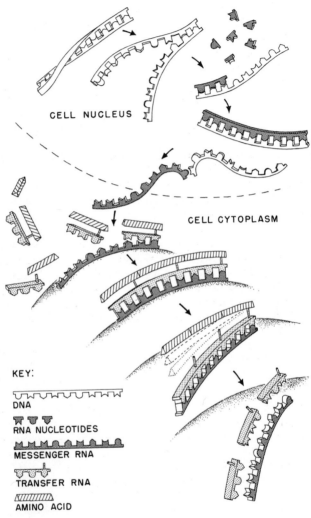

CELL NUCLEUS

CELL CYTOPLASM

KEY:

DNA

RNA NUCLEOTIDES

MESSENGER RNA

TRANSFER RNA

AMINO ACID

Figure 102

Transfer RNA's within the cytoplasm had already hooked up their appropriate amino acids. Like postmen who match the address on a package to just one house number among a chain of houses on a street, each transfer RNA in due course positioned an amino acid opposite a given nucleotide on the messenger RNA template.

The amino acids snapped together in a chain at the same time that the transfer RNA's unhooked the coupling that had enabled them to tow the amino acids into position.

The transfer RNA's then returned to the cytoplasmic sea, each free to combine again with an appropriate amino acid and repeat the process of transport to a template on the same or another ribosome.

And the newly made molecule of hemoglobin began to attract and incorporate the oxygen that the original DNA sequence ordered it to supply to the cell.

This is only a fraction of the chemical activity that takes place within a minute in cells so small that it would take a hundred of them to cover the period that marks the end of this sentence. As you read these words, chemical reactions similar to those we have just described (and diagrammed in *Figure 102*) are taking place in each of the billions of cells in your body.

Chapter 21

DNA AND RNA: MOLECULAR CODES

This message is a specific sequence, using letters from a 26-symbol alphabet:

MAKE HEMOGLOBIN

And this is the same message, transcribed into a two-symbol code (in this case, International Morse Code):

__ __ ·_ _·_ ····· · __ __ ___ __· ·_·· ___ _···· ·· _·

From the time that Watson and Crick postulated the structure of DNA, it was equally clear that a sequence in the four-symbol DNA code—this one, say

G T G C A A A A T A A T T G G G G G C T T C T T T T T

must somehow be transcribed by the cell into the 20-symbol amino acid alphabet, if a protein were to result.

It was early assumed, for reasons stated in the preceding chapter, that each DNA code word must be a triplet of nucleotides. But where was the proof? And if the code words *are* triplets, which ones in a given sequence make a word? In the example above, is GTG a word? Or does this triplet stand for "begin," perhaps, *after* which each successive triplet makes a word? Maybe the code is read GTG, TGC, GCA, etc.—with letters overlapping? Finally, does the cell read the code from a fixed point? And in what direction? From the GTG end or the TTT end?

For the past ten years, such questions have turned many scientists into code-breakers.[1] The favorite re-

---

[1] Some involuntarily. When it was announced in 1958 that G. W. Beadle had won a Nobel prize, he received the following telegram from the virologist Max Delbrück. After he had separated an unbroken line of 123 letters—A, B, C, and D only—into triplets, the message read:

search material has been a bacterial virus, the one that attacks colon bacilli, and the primary tool has been a class of chemical compounds called acridines. By a process not yet understood, these induce mutations in virus DNA (and presumably in other organisms, all DNA being the same) by inserting or deleting single DNA bases.

It is difficult not to break into gee-whiz prose in describing the achievements of investigators such as Seymour Benzer at Purdue and others who explore what is called "the fine structure"—that is, the molecular structure—of the living gene. *Figure 103,* for example, is a close-up of one section of DNA in a bacterial virus, as mapped by modern molecular biologists.

Figure 103

Each dark block represents the position in the chromosome of certain specific bits of the virus's total set of directions. (Incidentally, the light areas aren't empty; it's just not known what virus traits are encoded in those areas.) The dots represent nucleotides, although they are

---

ADB ACB BDB ADA CDC BBA BCB CDA CDB BCA BBA ADC ACA BDA BDB BBA ACA ACB BBA BDC CDB CCB BDB BBA ADE ADA ADC CDC BBA DDC ACA ADB BDB DDA BBA CCA ACB CDB ADC BDB BBA.

Beadle was hopelessly stuck until a botanist friend, David Smith, noted that BBA was the only triplet with a B in the middle, which suggested that it had a special function. It did: it marked the end of a word. This clue, by delineating word lengths, was the key to the solution. The message read: "BREAK THIS CODE OR GIVE BACK NOBEL PRIZE."

Beadle responded by sending an acknowledgment in a code of *his* devising, one which Delbrück also required help to break. The score thus seemed to be 1–1. But Delbrück's gamesmanship was superior. At a formal lecture Beadle gave in Stockholm following the Nobel ceremonies, he was presented with a 10-inch helix made of toothpicks, the tips of each "nucleotide" stained with one of four colors. Delbrück had airmailed it to the presiding officer. When decoded, this message read: "I AM THE RIDDLE OF LIFE. KNOW ME AND YOU WILL KNOW YOURSELF."

woefully out of scale. In order to depict this particular segment of the chromosome accurately, there should be about 32,000 dots shown: the grand total, for the entire chromosome, is around 200,000.

The largest of the mapped areas shown contains about 1000 nucleotides. You might think of them as a long column of soldiers, uniformed alike and evenly spaced. As they march down a road, they seem undifferentiated as to function. Yet they have an organizational identity, known to themselves and to those who command them. Upon demand, this army of individuals can sort itself into functional units of squads or platoons. The sub-groups of nucleotides which are shown in little boxes in *Figure 104* are such "squads" or "platoons." The numbers of nucleotides within each box vary, but those within any box work together as a unit. There are six such groupings in what we will here call Gene A, and ten such groupings in what we will call Gene B.

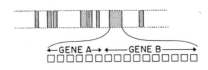

Figure 104

Knowing which traits in the virus are controlled by these genes, Francis Crick at Cambridge and other investigators have been able to induce mutations in the virus and then to combine the mutants in new ways for research purposes. In effect, they have made bacterial viruses to order, just as kennelmen have bred long-muzzle collies or poultrymen have bred big-breasted turkeys.

Here's a summary of their findings:

1. If viruses are exposed to acridine, and it knocks a nucleotide base out of Gene A (or adds one), Gene A is inactivated. But the function of Gene B is not impaired. And vice versa. (*See Figure 105.*) Therefore, there must be something in the code at the point where the genes join, some small barrier that gives them separate

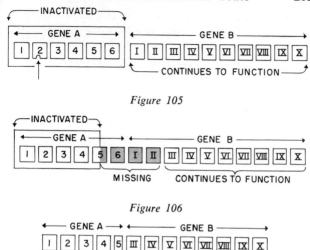

Figure 105

Figure 106

Figure 107

identity—just as the period at the end of a sentence signals the completion of a thought. What that barrier is has not been determined.

Gene A will also be inactivated and Gene B will still function in viruses which have lost the shaded segments of the two genes. In the case of this deletion, the molecule is correspondingly shortened, as in *Figure 107*. From such behavior one can conclude that the final segments of Gene A must be essential, like a man's heart; whereas the initial segments of Gene B can be done without, as when one loses a kidney.

2. However, if a virus which already lacks the final segments in Gene A and the initial ones in Gene B should also have a defect in one of the remaining nucleotide groupings in Gene A, *Gene B will not function*. The entire ribbon of DNA, from point 1 to point X, will be inactivated. (*See Figure 108.*) This can only mean that the elimination of the stop-start symbol between the two genes (whatever it is) has allowed the message to be read as one continuing sequence, and that the error in Gene A has

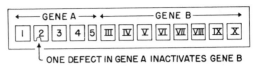

Figure 108

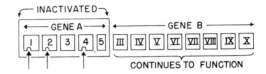

Figure 109

scrambled the code from that point onward. Therefore, it becomes clear that the DNA code is read from some fixed point.

3. But the function of Gene B is unimpaired if *three* deletions or *three* additions occur in Gene A (*see Figure 109*). Three is the magic number; the only other combination of deletions and additions that allows Gene B to function is one in which an addition and a deletion are close together and, in effect, cancel each other. Conclusion: the DNA code is read by the cell as triplet groups, and a scrambled message can be unscrambled only if enough nucleotides (threes or multiples of three) are added or deleted to bring it back into phase.

An analogy, using the English alphabet, envisions two machines, one of which is supposed to transmit the following message (which uses only four symbols—A, D, I, N):

D A D A N D N A N A I D A N N D A N A I D I D A

The receiving machine is capable of recognizing whether a certain sequence of letters makes sense. If the message comes through correctly, the machine will accept it, break it into triplets, punctuate it, and hand it over like this:

DAD AND NAN, AID ANN. DAN, AID IDA.

But suppose that something goes wrong at the sending end, and the first A is deleted.

D D A N D N A N A I D A N N D A N A I D I D A
↑

As it breaks the message into triplets, the receiving machine now reads nonsense:

DDA NDN ANA IDA NND ANA IDI DA

And if an extra letter had been inserted, the result would also be nonsense.

In either case, a red light will flash, the receiving machine will shudder and stop dead, and a scrambled message will be automatically fed into a wastebasket. Neither Ann nor Ida will get any aid.

Suppose, however, that *three* deletions are made in quick succession, so that the transmitting machine sends this message:

D D A N D N A A I D N N D A N A I D I D A
↑   ↑   ↑

The receiving machine will read nonsense at first, but the message will get into phase again at the end:

DDA NDN AAI DNN DAN AID IDA

—and Ida, at least, will get the help she needs.

This is precisely what happens when mutations that change the sequence of nucleotide bases interfere with the correct transmission of the DNA code.

The examples above reflect experiments in which acridine was the mutation-causing agent. But other chemicals also modify the molecular structure of DNA. Nitrites, for instance, disturb the hydrogen-bonding pattern of nucleotide pairs by changing molecular subgroups within them—NH_2 groups to OH groups. And high-energy radiation—whether from X-rays in a doctor's office or in the fallout of nuclear fission products from the stratosphere—can similarly scramble the code. It can knock out whole nucleotide bases; possibly it can even change one kind into another as a result of rearranging atoms within them.

In any case, if the molecule that is thus affected is in a sex cell and as a whole is not too badly damaged to reproduce, it will make a faithful copy of itself in its changed form and pass that change along to the next generation. If the altered code makes enough sense to the cell so that it can still make protein, the protein will be different from the protein made by the parent.

To illustrate, let's return to the sequence of DNA code given on the first page of this chapter. We now know that

G T G C A A A A T A A T T G G G G G C T T C T T T T T

will be read by the cell as

GTG CAA AAT AAT TGG GGG CTT CTT TTT

Additionally, we know that in order to make protein it must be transcribed into a complementary sequence of messenger RNA (uracil replacing thymine as the complement for adenine), so:

CAC GUU UUA UUA ACC CCC GAA GAA AAA

After which, each triplet will incorporate its appropriate amino acid complement (via transfer RNA) into a chain corresponding in sequence to the nucleotides of the original DNA. The end product will be whatever kind of protein the DNA specifies.

But what amino acid does *CAC* specify? Or *GUU?* Or any of the others? Linked together as we have shown them, what kind of protein do they make? The answers are beginning to arise from the work of scientists who have been investigating how the cell turns its raw material into protein.

Chapter 22

BREAKING THE CODE

A year before Arthur Kornberg succeeded in synthesizing DNA, his onetime teacher, Severo Ochoa, had pointed the way. Ochoa, Spanish-born biochemist at New York University, had begun to pry into the secrets of the nucleic acids by studying how phosphate is incorporated into them, and went from there to a detailed study and purification of the enzymes that actually engineer the construction.

In 1955, he put his purified enzyme into a test tube along with loose bits of the four RNA nucleotides (each with two extra phosphate groups attached)—and the enzyme organized these materials into an RNA chain that was chemically quite indistinguishable from a chain of RNA made by the living cell from which the enzyme had originally come.

Ochoa also made chains of just *one* kind of nucleotide

$$A\ A\ A\ A\ A\ A\ A\ A\ A\ A\ A\ A\ A\ A$$

or

$$U\ U\ U\ U\ U\ U\ U\ U\ U\ U\ U\ U\ U\ U$$

The one made up entirely of adenine is called Poly-A; the other, all uracil, is Poly-U. These are wholly artificial RNA's; at least, nothing like them is known in nature. But chemical analysis, X-ray diffraction, and other tests indicated that they have the "real" RNA structure.

Meanwhile, a fine new technique had been introduced into the laboratories of scientists whose interest is in protein synthesis. If you put colon bacilli into a mortar and gently grind them with finely powdered metal, its abrasive action ruptures the cells and releases the cell sap—but it doesn't immediately destroy the DNA, RNA, enzymes, and ribosomes in those cells. A solution of this sort is

called a "cell-free system." It is quite capable, given a shot
of high-energy phosphate, of taking amino acids and turning them into protein. If you label those amino acids
with radioactive carbon, you can follow the details of the
process by which protein is made.

In 1960, now that artificial RNA's and the cell-free
method of investigation were available, the curtain rose
on one of the most dramatic third acts in the history of
science. The principals were two young biochemists at the
National Institutes of Health—Marshall Nirenberg and
Heinrich Matthaei—who decided to find out if Ochoa's
Poly-U would incorporate amino acids into protein, and
what kind. Inasmuch as the only RNA triplet in Poly-U
is *UUU,* they knew they would begin to break the genetic
code if they could discover the amino acid that is specified
by *UUU.* Which is just what they did, in 1961.

Here is a more detailed account of their experiment:

They put *U U U U U U U U U U* chains of RNA
into twenty different cell-free systems, each containing the
full twenty amino acids; but in each vessel they labeled
a *different* amino acid with radioactive carbon. Protein
was formed in all vessels, which proved that synthetic
RNA could do the same job as natural RNA. And what
was the nature of that protein? In the vessel in which the
radioactive tag was on the amino acid phenylalanine, the
protein was radioactive. Furthermore, tests of protein
formed in all vessels showed it to be composed entirely of
phenylalanine. In other words, *UUU* must be an RNA code
word for phenylalanine, and the corresponding DNA sequence must be AAA, as in *Figure 110.*

DNA	AAA	AAA	AAA	AAA	AAA	AAA	AAA
	∣∣∣	∣∣∣	∣∣∣	∣∣∣	∣∣∣	∣∣∣	∣∣∣
RNA	*UUU*	*UUU*	*UUU*	*UUU*	*UUU*	*UUU*	*UUU*
	∨	∨	∨	∨	∨	∨	∨
PROTEIN	PHE	PHE	PHE	PHE	PHE	PHE	PHE

Figure 110

The ball, once started, rolled very fast. Within two
years, all possible combinations of the four RNA bases
had been used as Nirenberg and Matthaei had used
Poly-U; and at least one triplet and sometimes more had

been found to code for each of the twenty amino acids.
But even then the code was not fully broken.

The exact sequence of bases in the majority of triplets
—that is, how the "letters" are arranged within the "word"
—had to be determined. It was easy enough for *UUU*,
but were the two *G*'s and the *U* that were known to spell
glycine arranged as *GUG, GGU,* or *UGG*? The problem
was like the one that would face an investigator from another world, doing research about life on earth, who had
discovered that in one of the earth languages this object
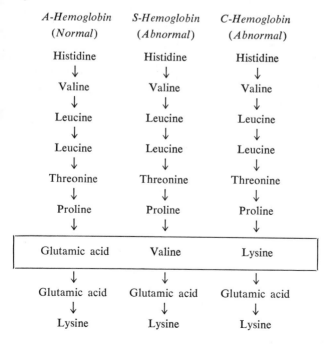 is symbolized by three letters. He knows *which*
three letters are used, but he doesn't know their order.
Until he finds out, he has to accept the possibility that the
might be a UCP, a UPC, a PUC, a PCU, a
CPU, or a CUP.

Following are two examples of molecular code-breaking:

A-Hemoglobin (Normal)	S-Hemoglobin (Abnormal)	C-Hemoglobin (Abnormal)
Histidine	Histidine	Histidine
↓	↓	↓
Valine	Valine	Valine
↓	↓	↓
Leucine	Leucine	Leucine
↓	↓	↓
Leucine	Leucine	Leucine
↓	↓	↓
Threonine	Threonine	Threonine
↓	↓	↓
Proline	Proline	Proline
↓	↓	↓
Glutamic acid	Valine	Lysine
↓	↓	↓
Glutamic acid	Glutamic acid	Glutamic acid
↓	↓	↓
Lysine	Lysine	Lysine

Look back to Chapter 15, to the account of V. M. Ingram's work on hemoglobin. He showed that the difference between normal and two abnormal hemoglobins is a difference of only one amino acid. This repeat of the chart showing amino acid linkages in hemoglobin indicates that the three amino acids which give these hemoglobins their distinctive character are glutamic acid, valine, and lysine.

Now let's examine the RNA code words for these three amino acids.

1. Glutamic acid contains one *G* and two *A*'s. It could therefore be written *GAA, AGA,* or *AAG.*

2. Valine contains one *G,* one *A,* and one *U.* It could be written *GUA, AUG, GAU, UAG, UGA,* or *AGU.*

3. Lysine contains three *A*'s. Its sequence therefore must be *AAA.*

Study the composition of those triplets. Is there any one point of difference between code words specifying glutamic acid (normal hemoglobin) and valine or lysine (abnormal hemoglobin)? Yes. In each, just one nucleotide —one letter of the code—is different. Instead of the *G,* *A,* and *A* that spells glutamic acid in normal hemoglobin, valine substitutes a *U* for one of the *A*'s; and lysine substitutes an *A* for the *G.* With what sequences, then, will one-nucleotide changes "fit"? One possibility is diagrammed below:

	Valine	*G U A*
		↑
Normal	Glutamic acid	*G A A*
		↓
	Lysine	*A A A*

The usefulness of such diagrams in code-breaking is obvious: when the sequence of any one of the triplets is known for sure, sequences of others may become known also.

Incidentally, this graphic representation of how single-nucleotide changes can alter the character of the amino acids squares beautifully with other findings of molecular biologists as to how mutations occur. S-hemoglobin and C-hemoglobin must have resulted from single-nucleotide changes in the section of DNA that carries the directions

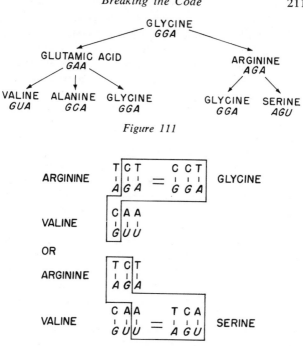

Figure 111

Figure 112

for the making of normal A-hemoglobin. The same changes would, of course, have been translated into RNA. And the RNA would have followed the new sequence in its assembly of amino acids—thus producing abnormal hemoglobin.

Our second example of molecular code-breaking also involves the matching of possible RNA triplet sequences to various amino acids. But the protein in this case is not the hemoglobin in blood but an enzyme made by the colon bacillus—which, in its normal form, incorporates the amino acid glycine at a particular position. Stanford's Ulf Henning and Charles Yanofsky have found two mutant versions of the enzyme, in one of which glycine has been replaced by glutamic acid, in the other of which glycine has been replaced by arginine. In addition, there are mutant versions of those mutants: enzymes which substitute valine or alanine for glutamic acid and enzymes which substitute serine for arginine. Finally—and bringing the wheel around full circle—both of the primary mutants have back-mutated to the normal glycine-containing form of their ancestor. This succession of changes is depicted in *Figure 111*—and please note that the code word given for each amino acid differs by only one letter from its predecessor.

Sharp-eyed readers will also note that *GUA,* the code word for valine in the colon bacillus enzyme, likewise specifies valine in hemoglobin (as shown in the diagram preceding *Figure 111*). But before you assume that this sequence is *the* way to spell valine, consider some other findings by Henning and Yanofsky:

They have shown (also in the colon bacillus enzyme) that in a given section of DNA the triplet which carries the directions for making valine can get itself tangled with a section which specifies arginine, the result being two new strips of DNA—one of which specifies glycine and the other, serine. This swap[1] is depicted in *Figure 112,* in which RNA code words appear in italics directly below the DNA triplets which initially specify the various amino acids. Keep your eye on valine.

That's right: in this instance, the code word for valine is *GUU.* Which is correct—*GUA* or *GUU*? Or both? In fact, might there not be even more alternative spellings?

We shall defer the answer for a paragraph or two, returning briefly to the work of Marshall Nirenberg. In association with Philip Leder, he has recently been able to introduce *single triplets* of messenger RNA into cell-free systems. These triplets, whether isolated from natural RNA or synthesized in the laboratory, behave just as they

---

[1] The Henning-Yanofsky experiment confirms, at the molecular level, crossing-over as a mechanism for genetic change. Morgan, Sturtevant, and Bridges had to check visible traits in the progeny (as described in Chapters 12 and 13) in order to determine that genes exchange when chromosomes happen to break and then mend themselves while lying across each other. Nowadays, chemical analyses can lead to the same conclusion.

do when part of a long ribbon of RNA in a living cell: associated with ribosomes, they act as templates against which amino acids are positioned by transfer RNA. In this case, of course, no protein is made; the usefulness of the technique is that, if the composition of the triplets is known, one can identify the amino acid for which each particular triplet is the code word. And (as a result of this and other research) it now appears that there are as many as *four* ways to spell valine. For the other amino acids, too, there are two or more code words.

The following table[2] shows the possibilities for which Nirenberg and his associates presented evidence in May 1965. Code words in boldface had been tested experimentally by the technique just described; those in lightface were predicted. *See table on page 214.*

Back to valine, now. The answer to our previously posed question is that this amino acid can be specified by *GUU, GUA, GUC,* or *GUG.* It is not a very satisfying answer to molecular biologists, however, because it indicates only what happens—not why. Perhaps each terminal letter-change represents a mutation in one strain of the colon bacillus whose enzyme structure is being studied in these experiments; but, if so, it must be a "silent" mutation—one of such neutral or passive character that it has no effect upon amino acid sequence. Whether this interpretation is correct remains to be seen. In any case, many scientists believe that there are subtle distinctions, not yet understood, among the several code words that specify the same amino acid—just as is true of the following sentences that say the same thing in different ways:

THOUGHTFUL FELLOWS ASSERT ALL CAN COMPREHEND GENETICS.
DISCERNING PERSONS AFFIRM ANY MAY UNDERSTAND HEREDITY.

Nor is "nonsense" necessarily the right word for the triplets so labeled in the following chart. Those that do not specify an amino acid may be found to carry other

[2] From the *Proceedings* of the National Academy of Sciences, May 1965.

RNA Triplet	Amino Acid	RNA Triplet	Amino Acid
UUU UUC	Phenylalanine	UGU UGC	Cysteine
UUA UUG	Leucine	UGA UGG	nonsense or Tryptophane
UCU UCC UCA UCG	Serine	UAU UAC	Tyrosine
		UAA UAG	nonsense
CUU CUC	Leucine or nonsense	CGU CCC CGA CCG	Arginine
CUA CUG	Leucine		
CCU CCC CCA CCG	Proline	CAU CAC	Histidine
		CAA CAG	Glutamine
AUU AUC	Isoleucine	AGU AGC	Serine
AUA AUG	Methionine	AGA AGG	Arginine or nonsense
ACU ACC ACA ACG	Threonine	AAU AAC	Asparagine
		AAA AAG	Lysine
GUU GUC GUA GUG	Valine	GGU GGC GGA GGG	Glycine
GCU GCC GCA GCG	Alanine	GAU GAC	Aspartic acid
		GAA GAG	Glutamic acid

instructions; in fact, there is evidence that *UAG* is the code word for "stop," and that its function is to terminate the making of a given protein chain.

These are only two of the small mysteries whose solutions still lie ahead. Nevertheless, the importance of the discoveries made to date cannot be overstressed. They have revealed the basic design of life, the way in which DNA directs our creation, growth, and functioning. What is to come is only an understanding of the details.

Therefore, as you study the final appearance in these pages of the segment of DNA that we have been using as our example (*see Figure 113*), keep in mind that medicine cannot yet correct an inherited anemia by switching particular nucleotides inside the patient's blood cells, or prevent the transmission of that anemia to his children by doing the same thing to his sex cells. But some day in the distant future, when the details of structure have been filled in, such intervention may conceivably be possible.

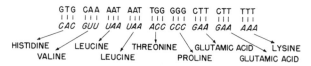

Figure 113

The recent developments in genetics have an analogy in the story of the Rosetta stone.

At the end of the eighteenth century, Egypt was a French possession. The fort of St. Julien was located in Rosetta (Rashid), a town that is close to Alexandria—and therefore one that in ancient times had both Greeks and Egyptians in its population. One August day in 1799, in the course of excavations necessary for repairs to the fort, a 4×2-foot black basalt stone was dug up. It was inscribed in hierogyphics, the picture language of the ancient Egyptian priests, which nobody alive could read. But—and this is what made its discovery an event of major importance—the stone also carried an inscription in Greek, which people *could* read. What if the stone had been inscribed for the convenience of a bilingual people, and one inscription were a translation of the other?

One *was* a translation of the other; and as a bonus, another form of ancient Egyptian writing was sandwiched in between them. The message in Greek provided the key to the translation of the other two; and records kept in man's first written language again became part of our cultural inheritance.

What has happened in genetics during the past decade has been the discovery of a Rosetta stone. The unknown language was the molecular one of DNA. Science can now translate at least a few messages written in DNAese into the chemical language of blood and bone and nerves and muscle. One might also say that the deciphering of the DNA code has revealed our possession of a language much older than hierogyphics, a language as old as life itself, a language that is the most living language of all— even if its letters are invisible and its words are buried deep in the cells of our bodies.

Chapter 23

SOME UNANSWERED QUESTIONS

The nuclei in our body cells—a total that runs into billions—contain duplicate sets of the same chromosomes. And yet, out of all the information coded in the DNA of those chromosomes, each cell uses only the part that pertains to its specialized role in the body. What causes this specialization is one of the major unanswered questions of biology.

In humans, for example, there is no readily visible differentiation among cells during the first few days after a sperm fertilizes an egg. But at some point before the fourteen-day mark is reached, the embryo has blood vessels and the beginnings of a spinal cord and brain. By the time the mother begins to suspect that she is pregnant, the embryo has a head and a heart, and the heart has begun to beat. When it is two months old and before it is an inch long, the embryo is recognizably human in both appearance and specialization of parts. What causes cells whose nuclei carry identical genetic information to use that information in so many diverse ways?

Nobody knows. But there are some clues.

There is a brown seaweed which, at the two-cell stage (and thus barely launched on life), differentiates into leaf-like fronds on top and root-like growths on the bottom. The embryologist Douglas Whitaker has found that if you expose the undivided egg to light from one side, the "roots" will appear on the dark side—regardless of whether the lighted side is the top, the bottom, or the midsection of the egg. If you bathe one side in sea water which is a little more acid than the sea water on the other side, the "roots" will appear on the more alkaline side. And if one side of the egg is warmer than the other, the "roots" will appear on the warmer side. Perhaps similar very early environmental differentials account for cell specialization in other organisms, including man.

Or perhaps something in the cytoplasm of the original single cell is the secret of later specialization of its offspring cells. We haven't said a great deal in this book about the role of cytoplasm, but it is much more than a protective wrapping for the nucleus and its chromosomes.

The zoologist John Moore has transplanted the nuclei of egg cells from one individual to another in frogs of the same species, without harming their development; but whenever his transplants come from another species, development fails. The geneticist Tracy Sonneborn's experiments with one-celled protozoa indicate that certain cytoplasmic structures must be present and in good working order or the dividing cell won't make replicas of them. Clearly, the cytoplasm must be complete; and it must be compatible with the nucleus. This is another way of saying that the cytoplasm contains specific biological information necessary for development.

You will remember that in cell division the nuclear membrane breaks down, thus making the cytoplasm the semi-liquid medium in which chromosome division and duplication take place. It is probable that something in the cytoplasmic environment, not the DNA itself, causes the cell's later differentiation of function, much as an alarm clock is set at one time but goes into action at another time.

There is no doubt at all that the cell's ability to carry out the chemical reactions specified by DNA is much modified by conditions external to DNA. We have already referred to acidity in cell sap as a determining factor in the coloration of certain flowers, and to low body temperature at the extremities as a necessary precursor to pigment formation in Siamese cats. Among human examples, there is the curious fact that both men and women have genes that cause baldness—but few women become bald. The reason is that male hormones apparently trigger the activity of the gene for baldness.

François Jacob and fellow workers at the Pasteur Institute in Paris have discovered that the colon bacillus has both "structural" and "control" genes. The latter act like switches that start or stop the activity of the structural genes, thus turning on or turning off the formation of the enzymes that actually do the work that DNA specifies. (Perhaps the geneticists of the early twentieth century were not so far off, after all, when they postulated the existence of "inhibitor" genes.)

Such control genes might initiate the formation of a certain kind of cell and then become permanently inactive. It is known that they sometimes control the manufacture of certain enzymes in accordance with the cell's "stockpile" level of raw material for the chemical reactions they catalyze. For example, when colon bacilli are grown on a medium containing the amino acid tryptophane—which they normally manufacture via a specific set of enzymes—their own production of those enzymes ceases.

Cancer is a non-specific disease which results when cells grow at an abnormal rate but never mature. "Control" genes out of order, perhaps? Do environmental influences short-circuit the cellular communications network so that the stop signal doesn't flash on at the right time? Did something go wrong in the cell cytoplasm, and if so, at what stage in the growth of the organism? There are hardly any answers, and they are partial. But you can see that the study of how genes control development and function merges into studies of how cells develop and function. Full knowledge of these processes awaits another generation of biologists.

Still ahead, too, is the answer to a most elusive question: What is memory? Our reasoning capacities and our ability to store information and then retrieve it exceed by far the similar capacities of any other species. That's why we're called *Homo sapiens*. Only man can add to the information he possesses at birth and pass it on in a cumulative fashion to subsequent generations. But how much information can a brain store? In what form do we keep it? Is the recollection of the sights and sounds and smells of a lifetime coded on some cerebral version of magnetic tape? When we want to recall something, how do we "scan" the tape? What is the role of the nucleic acids in the storage and retrieval of information? Nobody knows—although, again, there are clues.

One of the most exciting new specialties in science is psychobiology. It has joined physiologists, neurologists, and others in the biological sciences with psychologists and others in the social sciences—just as molecular biology has joined geneticists, biochemists, and physicists.

There is another question, too, for which many people —especially non-scientists—will continue to seek an answer. Is the prevailing theory as to life's origins and man's evolution, the one that has been set down in these pages, the correct one?

Answer: It is a theory that makes sense; there is more evidence in support of it than for any alternative; but it will necessarily remain a theory. Unwitnessed and unrecorded past events can never be documented by other than indirect evidence—and the events which the modern theory seeks to explain occurred anywhere from a million to well over six billion years ago.

Nobody, therefore, can prove or disprove beyond all doubt that the elements developed in turn from hydrogen, and that these combined in increasingly complex ways until one such combination could be said to be "alive." All that can with certainty be said is that the physical nature of the elements is known; if you rank them in order of increasing atomic complexity it becomes clear that they could have evolved in a step-by-step progression; and physicists have done experiments that demonstrate quite clearly that such a progression does occur when conditions are right.

Let's take the first sixteen elements and make a chart showing how many electrons they have and where those electrons are positioned. Electrons, you will remember from the second chapter, revolve around the nuclei of atoms within the confines of a series of concentric "shells." There are specialized terms that describe these shells, but for reasons of simplicity we are here labeling them A-E.

It should also be said that the elements listed below differ also in numbers of neutrons and protons in their nuclei; but since these differences do not invalidate the point, we have disregarded them.

Atomic Number	Element	A	B	C	D	E
1	Hydrogen	1				
2	Helium	2				
3	Lithium	2	1			
4	Beryllium	2	2			
5	Boron	2	2	1		
6	Carbon	2	2	2		
7	Nitrogen	2	2	3		
8	Oxygen	2	2	4		
9	Fluorine	2	2	5		
10	Neon	2	2	6		
11	Sodium	2	2	6	1	
12	Manganese	2	2	6	2	
13	Aluminum	2	2	6	2	1
14	Silicon	2	2	6	2	2
15	Phosphorus	2	2	6	2	3
16	Sulfur	2	2	6	2	4

There are many elements in addition to these, but one needs not go beyond 16 in a search for the raw materials needed for life. To make water, ammonia, methane, the sugars, certain amino acids, and the bases in nucleic acid, only four elements are required—hydrogen, carbon, nitrogen, and oxygen. With the addition of phosphorus and sulfur, proteins and the nucleic acids are possible. It does not stretch credulity to believe that over a span of several billion years it would have been possible for nature to have built a variety of complex molecules from only six elements.

That's a guess, of course. What is known is that in laboratory duplications of the presumed primeval atmosphere, amino acids as well as some building blocks of nucleic acid arise spontaneously from inorganic molecules of water, ammonia, and methane. In addition, the building blocks necessary to the formation of nucleic acid will arrange themselves into chains of DNA and RNA in a test tube—with no outside help except the assemblage into one spot of the proper ingredients. Bearing in mind our earlier statement that scientists can't make anything happen that couldn't happen without them, it can hardly be doubted that atoms combined into molecules and those molecules combined to make the key substances of life, billions of years ago, in much the same way that has now been witnessed in a test tube.

The imagination easily pictures several dozen . . . then several hundred . . . and finally several thousand nucleotides linked together and afloat in the ancient seas. The smallest viruses known today contain only about 5500 nucleotides. Conceivably, they are unchanged descendants of some very early form of life—even, perhaps, of the protogene. But that's a guess, too. Today's parasitic viruses might equally well be degenerate remains of organisms that flourished in complete independence at some midpoint in time past; or possibly they are "escaped" genes of present-day higher organisms.

There appears to be no predetermined course of evolution. It ebbs and flows like the tides. Lines of descent are not always from simpler to more complex forms; if simplification has advantages in a given environmental situation, then simpler forms will outbreed their competitors. Loss-of-function mutations are much more frequent than those that add or modify functions; in fact, a self-sufficient organism that's in the process of becoming a parasite would find a selective advantage in *not* doing things for itself. If the essentials of life are readily obtainable from its host, unused sections of its DNA would be available for specifying new functions through mutation and natural selection.

But complexity has its virtues, too. The more complex an organism, the more control over its environment it is likely to exercise. Nature's addition of a protein coat to a raw core of DNA would have been a step in that direction. So would have been the creation of the first cell. And the later coming-together of cells into colonies. And the development of multicellular organisms—which is what we are. At each of these stages, some organisms could have evolved "backward" (toward greater simplicity) and some "forward" (toward greater complexity). Man is one of the latter. The link between each evolutionary step would have been the DNA of each kind of organism. And the capability of DNA to carry ever-more-complicated sets of directions would have increased faster and faster with each increase in its quantity.

But, you may be thinking, only four kinds of nucleotides and only twenty amino acids form a very narrow base for the creation of all living things in their boundless diversity. Here, then, are some examples of how great a number of different large molecules can be constructed of relatively few subunits:

Suppose that a given protein molecule were to be made up of only one of each kind of amino acid (and bear in mind that a 20-unit protein molecule would be a very small one). Start with any one of the twenty. Any of the nineteen remaining could be in the second position in the chain. Any of the eighteen remaining could be in the third position. And so on: $20 \times 19 \times 18 \times 17 \times 16 \times 15 \times 14 \times 13 \times 12 \times 11 \times 10 \times 9 \times 8 \times 7 \times 6 \times 5 \times 4 \times 3 \times 2 \times 1$. Since each sequence adds up to a different kind of protein molecule, the variation inherent in the combination of only twenty units results in the possibility of over 2,432,902,008,176,640,000 different protein molecules—more than two quintillions.

However, our illustrative protein molecule was too small to be typical of real life. Suppose that it's a 150-amino acid protein (about the length characteristic of one protein chain in hemoglobin) that one is constructing. If all possible proportions and sequences of the twenty amino acids are assumed to be possible, the number of different proteins adds up to a total that is on the order of the number 1 followed by 215 zeros. This is trillions beyond any trillions that the human mind can comprehend. The best way to indicate how many possibilities it represents is to say that it is far more than the number of elementary physical particles—protons, neutrons, electrons, and some others we haven't mentioned in this book—that are estimated to exist in the entire known universe.

As for the nucleotides, when one takes four kinds and links them in units of three, only 64 combinations are possible. Yet if you put five billion pairs of these units into the nucleus of each human cell, having arranged them in all possible proportions and sequences, you end up with a sum in which the number 1 is followed by 30 *billion* zeros. Even if the majority of those possible arrangements were nonsense (in terms of their specifying some part of a viable organism), you can see that millions upon millions of workable arrangements are now available, have been in the past, or will be in the future.

In sum, then, there is a good case in support of the thesis that living things evolved from simple inorganic molecules to complex organisms as the result of small changes over countless millennia. Further, it is clear that the four kinds of nucleotides in DNA and the twenty kinds of amino acids in protein permit so much more variation among living things than now exists that opportunities for evolution are essentially unlimited.

What is not so clear is how to define the living state, and how to reconcile the teachings of religion with the teachings of modern molecular biology. With these questions we come to two for which absolute answers will perhaps never be found.

Life, according to Webster's Third New International Dictionary, is:

1a: Animate being: the quality that distinguishes a vital and functional being from a dead body or purely chemical matter . . . ; **b:** The principle or force by which animals and plants are maintained in the performance of their functions and which distinguishes by its presence animate from inanimate matter; **c:** The state of a material complex or individual characterized by the capacity to perform certain functional activities including metabolism, growth, reproduction, and some form of responsiveness or adaptability . . .

By any of the definitions above, men are alive. So are trout. And spiders. And earthworms. And bacteria. But what about viruses? They can reproduce and evolve, given the cells of one of those other organisms to grow in. They can't "perform certain functional activities including metabolism," but they certainly *can* direct metabolic processes for their own benefit. Given a choice between calling them animate or inanimate matter, wouldn't one be tempted to call them "animate"?

Viruses are essentially DNA with a protein coat, and that coat is primarily protective. So, if viruses are alive, couldn't one say that DNA molecules are alive, too—even artificial ones? Kornberg's artificial DNA's can reproduce, and presumably can evolve.

But Kornberg's artificial DNA's were made from "purely chemical matter," compounds that were inert until he put them together. Perhaps there is something hidden in them, a vital force unique to these particular compounds? If so, couldn't one say that adenine, thymine, guanine, and cytosine nucleotides are alive?

But they are composed of varying arrangements of elemental atoms—the same kind of atoms that compose the water you drink and the sugar you eat. As we said earlier, physicists have done experiments that have "created" the elements, step by step, from hydrogen. Are hydrogen atoms alive?

As you can see, there is no logical place to break the chain: hydrogen → the elements → chemical compounds → nucleic acids → proteins → viruses → bacteria → higher organisms. And since there is no logical place to break the chain, any definition of life must necessarily be arbitrary—given the present state of man's knowledge.

Perhaps a more exact way to phrase it would be: "In the continuum of being, is there a boundary between life and non-life?"

The question remains unanswered. But one is tempted to believe that science has made the question meaningless.

An even more difficult question is the one that goes this way: "Isn't the origin of life as explained by modern molecular biologists a denial of the existence of God?"

A good many people, hearing the story as it has been

told in this book, react like a certain freshman girl at the University of Chicago upon completion of a required course in biology. She said, "It's fascinating stuff. But I've decided that I don't believe it."

Hers—and perhaps yours, as you have read these pages —is an instinctive disbelief, born of our cultural inheritance. Somewhere in the recesses of the human mind is a certainty that there is a God, or gods, or an ordering intelligence which directs our affairs—and in the course of doing so has made us different from and better than other creatures. The Bible says, *"Be fruitful, and multiply, and replenish the earth, and subdue it: and have dominion over the fish of the sea, and over the fowl of the air, and over every living thing that moveth upon the earth."* (Gen. 1:28.)

Somewhere in the forefront of other human minds is a struggle to reconcile the findings of modern science with the teachings of a particular sect. *"And the Lord God formed man of the dust of the ground and breathed into his nostrils the breath of life; and man became a living soul."* (Gen. 2:7.) How can the Word be true as written, if at the same time it is also true that man is essentially an enormously complex bundle of chemicals that were put together in the course of a long process of evolution?

Nor has any of us wholly progressed beyond the Aristotelian view of the earth—and therefore of ourselves, as earthlings—as the center of the universe. We do not like being robbed of our uniqueness, of our superiority, of whatever divine spark was breathed into us. A view of our origin that makes us one with the cosmos is no recompense. Who wants to be made of the same stuff as a stone?

Lingering, too, is an ancient fear. Man should not try to penetrate the mysteries of heaven. *"And the Lord God commanded the man, saying, Of every tree of the garden thou mayest freely eat: But of the tree of the knowledge of good and evil, thou shalt not eat of it: for in the day that thou eatest thereof thou shalt surely die."* (Gen. 2:16–17.) If Pandora had only kept that box shut. If scientists would only leave well enough alone . . .

There is, however, no real conflict between the view of the origin of life as expressed in this book and as written in the Bible, unless every word in the Bible is taken literally. Few biologists, if any, consider the story of the creation of Adam and Eve as other than poetic description; but no biologist, or any other scientist, can flatly assert that God did *not* create the heavens and the earth, the sun and the stars, and every living creature that moves. Science studies the natural, the predictable, the repeatable, the verifiable. A supernatural event is by definition beyond the ken of science.

Besides, the ultimate question remains unanswered. *If all on earth evolved from hydrogen, where did the hydrogen come from?* Is it not as wondrous to envision a Creator Who made hydrogen, and gave it the capacity to evolve into man, as to envision Him making man from dust?

Chapter 24

A LOOK INTO THE FUTURE

The accumulation of human knowledge has been like a fireworks display, the initial course of each rocket being of long duration and steady flight by comparison to the resultant burst of light and rain of stars. Perhaps it is not surprising that men are still too bedazzled by the burst of knowledge to see what is revealed by its light.

Consider the historical timetable of change:

For perhaps a million years, evolving man and then modern man obtained food by hunting and gathering—in the beginning, by primitive means, later by the use of increasingly sophisticated implements and methods. But from the time, approximately 10,000 years ago, that modern man discovered he could raise his own food, one begins to count in thousands. Only 5000 years lie between the invention of agriculture and the rise of cities (from 4000 B.C. onward). The subsequent flowering of knowledge about the world we live in has caused the distance between milestones of human achievement to be counted in centuries; and then in decades.

From before the time of the Caesars to Victoria's reign, a man could travel no farther and no faster than a horse could go in a day or than wind would take a ship. Before Victoria's century was half done, man was traveling by rail and steamship; six decades after *that,* he was airborne; and in another six decades he was in outer space. Such accomplishments, all of which reflect a progressively more rapid accumulation of knowledge, have left mankind gasping. We're still in the driver's seat, all right, but we're showing the strain of too swift a passage.

Take biology. For hundreds of years we have consciously controlled the evolution of crops and livestock, breeding them to suit our purposes. Within recent years, we have accumulated enough knowledge so that we can now do the same thing with humans. No other species can direct its own evolution; and the capability is tempting. Hitler and others have already tried to breed a Superman, and many more would like to.

There are, however, a couple of stumbling blocks.

When you breed selectively, you discard those individuals whose qualities you don't want, or otherwise prevent their reproduction.

But let's say that the climate of moral opinion were to change to allow such selective breeding. The next problem would be: Who would decide what qualities Superman should have?

Almost everyone would agree that he ought to be intelligent. But the inheritance of native intelligence is only poorly understood. We do know that intelligent parents don't always produce intelligent offspring; and since a number of months have to pass after birth before one can tell whether a youngster is inherently intelligent, we'd have a considerable number of rejects who would not be allowed to reproduce.

Besides, what *kind* of intelligence do we want? There are people whose brainpower runs on conventional tracks, and others who organize information in entirely new ways. These latter ones are the creative types. Is their creativity inherited, or is it the result of environment? Nobody knows. Maybe some of those infant rejects would have developed into the innovators without whom any society is sterile. . . .

And what about Superman's superficial characteristics? Given the state of the world today, the determination of his skin color alone could start a war. Should he be tall or short? Maybe he ought to be bred in a size that would fit into a space capsule better than the present model. It would be a convenience if he didn't need sleep. And since he'd have to read so much, wouldn't it be useful to lengthen his eyeballs? Then he wouldn't need glasses for close work.

Finally, having gotten him, what if conditions on earth

were to change so drastically that he turned out to be as ill-adapted as the dinosaurs?

No. Man knows enough but is not yet wise enough to make man. And therefore our best course is to assure maximum evolutionary flexibility for future generations by maintaining a high degree of wholesome genetic diversity among men.

There's an important adjective in that last sentence: "wholesome." Although mankind does not consciously direct its evolutionary future, we unconsciously do so in a limited way—mostly as a result of ignorance of the consequences of actions which have genetic effects.

It is estimated that in the United States one baby boy in seventeen births is color-blind. Over 50,000 diabetics are born each year. There are 400 annual births of hemophiliacs. With each additional year, cystic fibrosis disables an additional 2400 individuals, and the number of those who suffer from muscular dystrophy increases by an additional thousand.

Something like 6000 newborn each year are Mongolian idiots. Retinoblastoma, an eye cancer that is fatal unless the eyes are removed, occurs in one birth in 20,000. A list of other inherited diseases or disorders could go to several hundred entries. All told, approximately 5 per cent of babies—that is, one in every twenty—are born with a potential genetic defect of some sort, minor to gross in effect. The total number of people so affected may now number as high as 150,000,000, worldwide.

In each case, the cells of the affected person contain one or more segments of DNA in which the code has been changed—perhaps long ago, in the egg or sperm cell of some forebear, perhaps in the immediately preceding generation. In each case, the carrier of a faulty message may pass it on to his children in accordance with Mendel's laws. And those whose cells contain that message will in turn have to adjust to disabilities as slight as dependence on someone else to pick the tie they'll wear today, or to chronic illnesses as devastating as Huntington's chorea or as expensive to treat as hemophilia.

Now that medicine has brought the nutritional and infectious diseases so largely under control, genetic diseases loom relatively larger in importance. There was a time when they did not build up in frequency with each successive generation, since natural selection took them out of the population as fast as new mutations occurred. (That's a euphemism for saying that victims of many inherited diseases didn't live long enough to reproduce.) But diabetics now have insulin, hemophiliacs have blood-clotting drugs, and babies who can't tolerate galactose survive on other sugars: in short, there are now large numbers of people whose genetic diseases have been circumvented—*not* cured—and who therefore pass them on to future generations.

The resulting buildup in frequency will be very slow. It may require thousands of years in the case of any one genetic disease to reach an incidence of one affected person per thousand. But if the total number of individuals whose debilitating inherited diseases have been circumvented becomes large, the social burden that they impose may become serious.

It is already so in small societies where much inbreeding occurs. For example, among the Caribe Cuñas—a tribe of Central American Indians—seven babies in every thousand are albinos. Retinitis pigmentosa, an inherited eye defect that causes the retina to become opaque, has been reported in the small, clannish colony on Tristan da Cunha. In a non-industrialized society like this one—where fishing and agriculture are basic to the economy—what is there for a blind man to do? How many blind men can a colony of fewer than 300 people absorb?

An obvious solution to problems like these would be for affected individuals to voluntarily refrain from conceiving children, and to build their families via adoption. But to make such a decision is rarely easy, since it is frequently impossible to know which two of any four genes of the parent have been or will be inherited by a given child.

If your first-born were an albino would you risk a second pregnancy if a counselor in a genetics clinic told you that the chance of a second child being similarly afflicted were 1 in 4? And here's a more difficult one: What if you've had no children, but your much older brother's recent marked mental deterioration has just been diagnosed as Huntington's chorea, an inherited disease that shows up in maturity? If you are enough younger so that the disease hasn't had a chance to express itself in you, you would now know that you have a 50–50 chance of carrying the gene, and any children you might conceive would have a 50–50 chance of acquiring the disease (since the gene is dominant). Should you risk it?

Such decisions are difficult even for people capable of the voluntary restraint that the odds sometimes indicate. Many people, of course, are incapable of restraint—especially if a condition is treatable and the baby has a good chance of growing up able to lead a normal life.

There may well come a time when even as humane a society as ours will find that people with inherited diseases and disabilities constitute a social burden so great relative to our resources that we will be forced to limit what most of us consider one of our inalienable individual rights—the right to bear children without reference to the consequences for society. We already do this to a limited extent when we isolate certain categories of feeble-minded, insane, and criminal individuals —and thus prohibit their reproduction.

The world society of mankind has already added in small measure to its future burden of genetic defects by exposure of large populations to high-energy radiation— but no one knows precisely how heavy that burden will be.

Since the children born to A-bomb survivors at Hiroshima and Nagasaki are neither monsters nor show a marked increase in genetic disease, non-scientists were inclined to draw deep sighs of relief when it was first reported that "no statistically significant increases in direct genetic effects have been detected."

Such reports do *not* mean that there are *no* effects. For one thing, recessive mutations are hidden in the first generation. For another, the numbers of children observed are small, and there are no strictly comparable unexposed populations to serve as controls. Hence it is difficult to know whether, or by how much, the mutation rate among A-bomb survivors has exceeded the normal rate.

The data gathered on the A-bomb children *do* show that the genetic sensitivity of men to radiation cannot be much higher than that of mice; otherwise the studies already carried out would have demonstrated it. During the years that the A-bomb children have been growing up, there have come and gone many generations of mice whose forebears were exposed in laboratories to radiation equivalent to that received by Japanese survivors of the A-bombs. Increased incidence of cataract, more sterility, and shorter life spans are characteristic of descendants of the irradiated mice. Nevertheless—since mice are not men —it is impossible to predict with certainty whether descendants of the A-bomb children will show genetic damage like that already observed in mice. It is reasonable —and prudent—to assume that they will.

The subject of mutation as a result of fallout has been much beclouded by emotion, absence of definite information, and occasional misinterpretation. The fallout of carbon 14, for example, has caused much concern because its long half-life of over 5000 years[1] prolongs its effects for many generations. Another product of nuclear explosions that can cause mutations is cesium 137, which has a half-life of about thirty years. It should be stressed that the release of these and other man-made radioactive materials has not introduced radiation hazards to a world previously without them: carbon 14, for instance, has for millions of years been naturally formed by the action of cosmic ray neutrons on nitrogen. The basic point at issue in discussions of fallout, therefore, is that it has *added* to the natural (or "background") radiation that man cannot control or escape.

---

[1] Half-life means that half of a substance's radioactive molecules lose their radioactivity during the period of time mentioned.

How much extra radiation was introduced into man's environment during the years of testing before the test-ban treaty of 1963? Rather than give quantitative estimates expressed in the units of measurement used by chemists and radiologists (which require a great deal of explanation), we prefer to indicate the possible effect of fallout upon living organisms by comparing it to natural radiation. The unit of measure we will use is the rad,[2] which measures the biological effect of radiation.

Natural radiation is estimated to deliver an average dose of 1/10th of a rad per year to the world population. This is a very low level of exposure. A chest X-ray (a big-plate X-ray, the kind one gets in a doctor's office or in a hospital) delivers 1/20th to 1/10th of a rad. (The small-plate version given by a Chestmobile requires higher exposure, delivers about 1/2 a rad.) The 1964 report of the United Nations Scientific Committee on the Effects of Atomic Radiation estimates that the amount of carbon 14 and cesium 137 which were added to the atmosphere by bomb tests will—over the period of time it takes them to decay—increase the dose which may cause mutation by less than another 1/10th of a rad. In other words, the over-all increase will be very small.

Now, what of the mutation rate? The Committee on the Biological Effects of Radiation, appointed by the National Academy of Sciences, has estimated that bomb tests to date may have raised the mutation rate, worldwide, by 1/10th of 1 per cent. That is, the extra radiation from fallout may add 3000 people each year to the number— some three million, worldwide—who are born with or will develop significant genetic defects. Yet even this carefully reasoned estimate as to number of individuals whose genes might be altered by fallout is subject to a large margin of uncertainty. It could not be otherwise—for the mutation rate produced in man at *any* level of radiation is not accurately known, much less at the low level of exposure produced by fallout.

2 A rad is "a unit of absorbed dose of ionizing radiation equal to an energy of 100 ergs per gram of irradiated material."

This is a good point at which to discuss the other kind of damage from high-energy radiation, that which can cause disease but does not necessarily cause mutations in sex cells (the only ones that can be transmitted to succeeding generations).

In addition to carbon 14 and cesium 137 (which affect both health and heredity), the fission products with localized effects on the body include strontium 90, whose half-life is twenty-five years; and iodine 131, whose half-life is only eight days. Strontium 90, which the body does not easily distinguish from calcium, is incorporated into bone, where it may possibly cause cancer, including leukemia (this latter because blood is manufactured in the bone marrow). Iodine is normally stored in the thyroid gland, which is in the throat; excessive amounts of radioactive iodine therefore may cause thyroid cancer.

Radioactive materials are incorporated into the human body in indirect ways. For one example, they filter down from the upper atmosphere, settle on grass, are ingested by cows along with that grass, and eventually make their way into the tissues of people who drink milk given by those cows. The degree of worldwide contamination varies greatly, in accordance with the latitude at which an explosion took place, wind patterns, and rainfall; the Northern Hemisphere, for example, has received four times as much strontium 90 as the Southern Hemisphere. (*See Figure 114,* adapted from the previously cited United Nations report.[3]) If no more atmospheric tests had occurred

---

[3] As we said earlier, in order to indicate amounts of radioactive substances it is necessary to explain units of measure, which we have judged to be too complicated for purposes of this book. To the average reader, we will simply say that the amount of strontium graphed in *Figure 114* and to be recorded in a following chart is small. For others, here are the essential facts without detailed explanation:

Strontium-deposit in *Figure 114* is measured in megacuries per square kilometers per month. A curie (named after the discoverers of radioactive elements) is "a unit quantity of any radioactive nuclide in which exactly 3.7×10^{10} disintegrations occur per second." A megacurie is one million curies. Later, you will find some amounts measured in picocuries, each of which is a trillionth of a curie.

after the test-ban treaty, the expectation would have been for a progressive decline of strontium 90 at a rate proportional to its own rate of decay.

According to the same United Nations report, fallout produced before 1963 has added to the world population

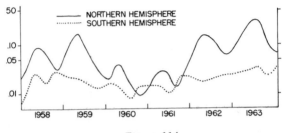

Figure 114

the risk of cancer including leukemia as expected from about 1/4th of a rad additional exposure to bone and 1/5th of a rad additional exposure to bone marrow. Again, this means that the over-all increase will be very small—unless atmospheric testing resumes on a large scale. Neither France nor Communist China, both of which have atomic weapons, are bound by the test-ban treaty; and other nations are working hard to become nuclear powers. To the extent that atomic weapons are again exploded in the atmosphere, the currently dropping level of fallout will rise again.

You should bear in mind, however, that the figures given in preceding paragraphs are averages. For example, the surface deposition rate of strontium 90 as shown in *Figure 114* means only that the total amount of strontium that fell over a certain area per month averaged out at a certain amount per unit of land. One particular acre within that area could have received more than average, another particular area less than average—and its effect would have differed according to whether or not the area was populated or utilized for food purposes. It is the exposure of specific individuals or groups to radioactivity far in excess of the "average" that has engendered much of the emotion affecting the subject of fallout hazards.

The authors of this book find it difficult to preserve a dispassionate tone at this point, because the damage (however small) that has resulted from the ingestion of radioactive fallout products has been concentrated within two groups that are the least able of any in world society to defend themselves: babies and young children, and the semi-primitive peoples of the Arctic.

Children get bigger doses because they are more likely to drink milk. And the potential harm is greater: in the case of strontium, for example, developing teeth and bones have greater need for calcium than teeth and bones that are already formed, hence the young body will incorporate more strontium than the older one. The chart below, taken from data in the United Nations report we have been citing, shows how (in bone samples taken from children who live in New York) strontium deposits rose in proportion to degree of bomb-test activity.

	Children Aged up to 1 Year	Age 1 to 2	Age 2 to 3	Age 3 to 4
1961	3.43	2.67	2.34	2.05
1962	3.81	3.05	2.68	2.61
Last six mos., 1963	6.81	9.84	5.03	3.41

(Quantities shown here are measured in picocuries per gram of calcium in bone.)

The sharp rise characteristic of the final months of 1963 in New York has been noted elsewhere in the world where similar records of bone samples are being kept. No one knows whether the amount of strontium which has been built into the bones of millions of children—and which will emit small amounts of radiation throughout their lives—is sufficient to cause malignancies. Scientists who have interested themselves in such matters are reasonably sure that the incidence will be very low.

And what about radioactive iodine? The Federal Radiation Council considers an average dose to the thyroid of 1/2 a rad to be "safe" for the general population. The "maximum tolerable dose" has been set by the same group at 1 1/2 rads. These limits would have to be revised downward if limits were being set for children, because a child's thyroid is smaller and, inasmuch as exposure begins earlier in life, is exposed to radiation longer.

Yet on at least seven occasions between 1952 and 1962, children in Washington County, Utah—150 miles east of the nuclear testing grounds in Nevada—received doses of radioactive iodine to their thyroid glands (by way of contaminated milk) in amounts ranging from 5 to 100 rads. Some 3000 children in Utah and Nevada are estimated to have received similarly excessive doses, as a result of which it is estimated that 10 to 12 cases of thyroid cancer may possibly develop.[4] Statistically, that's not much—only 3/10ths of 1 per cent. But parents of children in Washington County are, understandably, not much comforted by knowing that "only 3/10ths of 1 per cent" of those exposed—or perhaps fewer—will develop thyroid cancer. The burning question in their minds is: Will *my* child be affected? Only time can answer them.

During the great debate which preceded the cessation of American, British, and Russian atmospheric bomb tests in 1963, citizens who felt strongly that nations who have weapons are likely to use them were inclined to overstate or otherwise dramatize the genetic and other health hazards resulting from weapons testing—as an argument for disarmament. Citizens who felt strongly that we can't keep the peace unless we have a powerful deterrent were inclined to minimize the hazard. Those who argued the moral issue—"What right does any nation have to drop fallout on innocent bystanders?"—had, in many respects, the strongest case for cessation of nuclear tests; but they had less impact on national policy than the others.

The present *degree* of contamination is of little consequence if one wishes to argue against bomb tests on moral

[4] From records kept by the St. Louis Citizens Committee for Nuclear Information, many of whose members are scientists on the faculty of Washington University, St. Louis. The organization has analyzed the fallout of atomic tests in Nevada since 1951, and has regularly published the findings in a journal called *Nuclear Information* (recently renamed *Scientist and Citizen* and broadened in scope).

grounds. The world can "take" much more radioactivity than is in the atmosphere now or is likely to be in the near future. Based on the estimate of the National Academy of Science's committee—that the mutation rate has been raised so far by only 1/10th of 1 per cent—we have a long way to go before the mutation rate doubles; and as a species we could no doubt survive much more than a doubling. Nor can fallout so far have increased the expected incidence of radiation-induced malignancies by more than an amount so small that it cannot be measured experimentally. The important point is that in matters of morality, numbers don't count. Can anyone argue that it's all right to induce thyroid cancer in children because only 3/10ths of 1 per cent of those exposed may develop it?

All around the world, certain peoples who live near the Arctic Circle—among them, North American Indians and Eskimos, Laplanders of northern Sweden and Finland, and Asian tribes at the top of Soviet Siberia—have for some years been exposed to radioactivity in excess of accepted "safe" levels. That's because their main source of food is the caribou, a reindeer that feeds on lichens which have been heavily salted with cesium 137. The 1964 United Nations report says that some Lapps and Eskimos now have a body content of cesium 137 that is 100 times higher than the world average. All told, these various Arctic tribes number perhaps 100,000 people. Their "incidence" in the world population is small. Is it all right, then, for their bigger neighbors to contaminate their food and endanger their health?

The advice of an earlier United Nations Scientific Committee on the Effects of Atomic Radiation (1962) still makes good sense, but one wonders if the right people are listening. Here it is:

"Radioactive contamination of the environment resulting from explosions of nuclear weapons constitutes a growing increment to worldwide radiation levels. This involves new and largely unknown hazards to present or future populations; these hazards, by their nature, are beyond the control of the exposed persons.

"The Committee concludes that all steps designed to

minimize irradiation of human populations will act to the benefit of human health. Such steps include the avoidance of unnecessary exposure to medical, industrial, and other procedures for peaceful uses on the one hand, and cessation of contamination of the environment by explosions of nuclear weapons on the other."

The reference in this statement to "medical, industrial, and other procedures" brings up a form of man-made radiation with which most of us are so familiar that we are slightly startled to realize that it *is* radiation and therefore potentially harmful. Yet there is no estimate of how many cells—reproductive or otherwise—have been unwittingly damaged in the course of recent years by indiscriminate use of X-rays.

There was a period when some dermatologists used radiation to treat acne; when it was customary to X-ray pregnant women to determine the fetal position of the infant; and when dentists and others who used this powerful diagnostic tool did not realize that they and their assistants should be shielded along with the patient.[5] Older readers will remember, too, the shoe store X-ray machines of the 1920's, over which so many of us spent delighted minutes looking at our naked bones within our new shoes—while the same radiation that revealed those bones flowed upward unchecked.

The risks are now recognized, however. Used properly for diagnostic and therapeutic purposes by competent and well-informed medical practitioners, the benefits of X-ray can now be achieved with minimal risk. To employ them may be essential for health and even life; so don't refuse them "on principle." Choose your doctor well, assure yourself that he is up to date in his knowledge of radiation hazards—and then don't try to second-guess him.

[5] The death rate from leukemia, a cancer that destroys red blood cells, now seems to be significantly higher among radiologists than in the general population. In the limited but best data available, there are 12 deaths from this disease to 4 expected in a population of non-radiologists of similar age distribution. For details see an account by E. B. Lewis in the journal *Science*, December 13, 1963.

Here ends our discussion of the dangers inherent in high-energy radiation.

In summary, no one can predict exactly how twentieth-century exposure of large populations to increased radiation will affect either the health of the individuals exposed or the future evolution of mankind. It will cause *some* mutation beyond that which occurs naturally, and the increase will be small percentagewise. However, since most mutations—perhaps 99 out of 100—impair the functioning of an organism rather than improve it, the sensible course of action is to hold to a minimum mankind's use of *any* mutation-causing agent.

Mankind has a much graver problem than any foreseeable increase in mutation rates. Far more important to the future of *Homo sapiens* is his current failure to limit his differentially expanding populations. This will be a significant evolutionary factor in the world of the not-so-very-distant future.

The reference here is not to total numbers. Demographers are already warning that the present world population of three billion may double by the year 2000, with a possible depression in standards of living. Having more people in the world than can be fed would inevitably result in the death of many individuals because of famines, revolutions, and wars. But such deaths would not necessarily affect the character of the entire human species.

Differential expansion of populations will. What this phrase means is that the net reproductive rate (births less deaths) of one population exceeds that of another. And the result of such disparity, if it continues over a long enough period of time, is that one population will replace the other.

Take two types of bacteria, for instance. Suppose that Type A reproduces just rapidly enough to maintain a constant population whereas Type B doubles each hour. After one hour, Type B will outnumber Type A by two to one. In ten hours—that is, in ten generations—Type B will have increased slightly more than a thousandfold—1024 times, to be exact. And in twenty hours, the faster-reproducing form will outnumber the slower one by more than a million to one. For all practical purposes, Type B will then have replaced Type A.

Among humans, a 3 per cent increase per year adds up to a doubling of population in slightly less than 25 years; and there are a number of human populations that now have net reproductive rates at or near this level. If present rates of increase should be maintained for twenty generations—a rather unlikely but not inconceivable state of affairs—the effective replacement of static segments of the population by those that are doubling with each generation could occur within 600 years.

Compare the lists below.

Country	Annual Rate of increase	Country	Annual Rate of increase
Brazil	2.4–2.8% *	Australia	1.7%
Ceylon	2.6	Canada	1.9
China (Free)	3.1	Denmark	.6
China (Communist)	2.3*	England	.9
Costa Rica	4.2	France	.9
Guatemala	3	India	1.8
Malaya	3.1	Italy	.8
Iran	2.5–2.8*	Japan	.9
Jamaica	3	Netherlands	1.3
Pakistan	2.6–3*	Norway	.8
Paraguay	3–3.5*	Poland	1.1
Puerto Rico	2.7	Portugal	.8
Sudan	3.3*	Sweden	.3
Tunisia	3.3	U.S.A.	1.2
Uganda	2.2	U.S.S.R.	1.5
Venezuela	2.5–3.2*	Yugoslavia	1.4

* These rates of growth are estimates. Figures have been taken from the United Nations' Demographic Yearbook (1963) and from *Comparative Demographic Computations,* a publication of the Population Research and Training Center, University of Chicago (June 1964).

Nathan Keyfitz, University of Chicago sociologist, divides the peoples of the world into three groups: those that live in highly developed, densely settled countries; those that live in developed but more sparsely settled countries; and those that live in underdeveloped countries. Death rates everywhere do not now vary to a significant extent, but birth rates *do;* and birth rates are progressively higher in each of Professor Keyfitz's three groups. Here they are, with current population estimates:

	Crowded, Developed Countries	Spacious, Developed Countries	Underdeveloped Countries
Birth rate	Under 20 births per 1000 people	20–30 births per 1000 people	Over 30 births per 1000 people
Total pop.	Half a billion	Half a billion	Two billion

Now let's suppose that the crowded, developed countries (essentially all those in Europe, plus Japan) were to increase their populations at the rate of 3/4 of 1 per cent per year—close to an average of their present rate of increase—for approximately another 100 years. Let's suppose, too, that the developed countries with a lot of land (the United States, Australia, and the Soviet Union are typical) increase at about their present rate—1.5 per cent per year for another 100 years. And, finally, let's suppose that the underdeveloped countries increase at the rate of 3 per cent a year for the same period. Here is how world populations would then compare:

	Crowded, Developed Countries	Spacious, Developed Countries	Underdeveloped Countries
Total population, 1964	Half a billion	Half a billion	Two billion
Total population, 2064	One billion	Two billion	Sixteen billion

This drastic shift in populations could occur, please note, in only 100 years. Grandchildren and great-grand-children of those who are celebrating their 21st birthdays this year will have to cope with the problems presented by such a differential growth of populations—if it continues.

Every demographer who makes such projections hopes, with Professor Keyfitz, that "the situation they portray will not materialize." But the nations of the world have been warned for many years now as to what lies ahead—and differential rates of increase have not greatly altered.

True, individual nations have had some success in reducing their rate of increase. Free China stood at 4.4% in 1956, for example, hence her present 3.1%—frightening though it is—represents a considerable drop. India is making heroic efforts in this direction. But the reason, in each case, is in the interests of national welfare—to reduce the number of mouths that must be fed. No nation can force (or, probably, persuade) any other nation to limit its population growth on the basis that it is desirable to maintain population distribution as it now is. The only way to go at it would seem to be for the industrialized nations (if they want to maintain something like the status quo) to help the underdeveloped nations become *developed* nations—and quickly.

If, for example, the total population of South America continues to double every thirty years whereas the total population of North America increases at its present lower rate, there will be significant political, social, and economic changes in the Western Hemisphere within a century. We are making no value judgments here, no comment as to whether the changes would be good or bad. The point is that there would be significant changes.

The same thing can be said of man's evolutionary future. Nobody knows what of value may have been lost to us when, in prehistoric times, the Neanderthals were replaced by our ancestor Cro-Magnons. Nor whether it is good, bad, or unimportant (in the evolutionary sense) that certain tribes of American Indians are now in the process of vanishing.

Will it matter to the species if *Homo sapiens* of, say, 2465 has inherited more genes from people of one nationality or one race than from another? Costa Ricans or

Tunisians may or may not be better adapted to the physical environment of earth and more capable of conserving mankind's cultural heritage than Norwegians or Japanese. The Caucasians of European stock, the Congoids of Africa, or the Mongoloids of Asia may or may not have differential evolutionary *value*. But there is no doubt that differential reproductive rates, if unchecked, will have an evolutionary *effect*.

Something should probably be said at this point specifically about the American Negro, since the facts about him have been seasoned with so much myth. It is true that the Negro birth rate in the United States is currently twice as high as the birth rate among whites, but —again—nobody can say whether a higher proportion of Negroes in the future population (should the differential birth rate continue) would be good, bad, or immaterial.

In our present emotionally supercharged atmosphere, some whites base their attitudes toward Negroes on a belief that the adaptation of Negroes to the American social and economic environment is the result of inherent qualities. One hears, for example, that Negroes are not as educable, as industrious, as physically fit—or whatever quality is being compared—as whites because "the races are genetically different."

The answer to this is that every individual of whatever race is genetically different from every other individual (unless he has an identical twin). What matters is not the fact of difference, but whether the differences are significant in survival as individuals, as nations, or as a species. As of now, there is no compelling evidence that any race is genetically superior to any other race—in health, in behavior, or in ability to acquire a specific cultural pattern. And, on the domestic scene, there is considerable evidence that the alleged cultural inferiority of Negroes is the result of less favorable opportunity, on the average, for education and employment, and their being raised in poorer social and economic environments than whites. One way to settle the question is to equalize Negro and white opportunity and environment—and *then* compare intelligence and achievement.

Nor is this essentially a racial problem. Numerous minority groups are similarly handicapped: American Indians; many Mexican-Americans living in the West and Southwest; the poor whites who eke out an existence on marginal land in Appalachia or the Deep South; the small army of migrants who, with their families, follow the harvests that require hand labor; and those among the various groups of non-English-speaking immigrants who have no marketable skills. The circumstance that characterizes all such minorities is that they are physically isolated—by chance or design—from the mainstream of American society, and thus have no opportunity to acquire the cultural pattern of the majority.

Many modern studies[6] indicate that the years from birth to school age are of critical importance in any child's acquisition of his society's culture. If, for example, a child —whether of Puerto Rican, Tennessee "hillbilly," or Negro parents—is reared in an inner-city ghetto in a home where middle-class American English is neither read nor spoken, his ability to learn at school may be irreversibly damaged. Personality factors stemming from the same environment also affect such children's ability to succeed in school systems based on a different kind of cultural inheritance.

This problem will be enormously difficult to solve, because what is necessary is to interrupt somehow the chain of cultural inheritance that produces minorities who are literally incapable of competing with the majority. To equalize the opportunity of the two groups may require the widespread establishment of nursery schools at which, from age two (or even younger), children born into subcultures such as those mentioned can acquire, from a source outside the home, the same cultural inheritance that the average middle-class American child acquires in *his* pre-school years.

6 A large number of these have been summarized in *Stability and Change in Human Characteristics,* by Benjamin S. Bloom (New York: John Wylie & Sons, 1964).

What is the solution to such problems? Is it up to "the government" to find answers? The government is only an extension of ourselves. Then how about turning to "the experts" for guidance? Fine, if their guidance remains within their field of specialty. Educated men—and scientists in particular—should be, and usually are, a bit more objective than other men. But even the best of them have emotional biases that affect their attitudes toward social problems. Because a man is a brilliant research scientist or physician or lawyer or economist or educator does not necessarily make him more competent than any other intelligent man to resolve problems outside his area of expertise. Man as a species is a jack-of-all-trades, but no individual man knows everything about everything; and however much we may want someone to make up our minds for us, there is no escape from doing it ourselves—if we want to preserve the structure of our society as it is at present.

Happily, we have available to us a splendid tool for this purpose: the human brain. It enables us not only to accumulate knowledge but also to modify behavior in accordance with what we have learned. It took us a million years of trial and error to forge it, but the finished product is a beauty. All we have to do now is to use it.

INDEX

ANCHOR BOOKS

ANCHOR BOOKS

Science Study Series (continued)